Belknap's Waterproof ALL NEW EDITION

CANYONLANDS River Guide

Bill & Buzz Belknap / Loie Belknap Evans

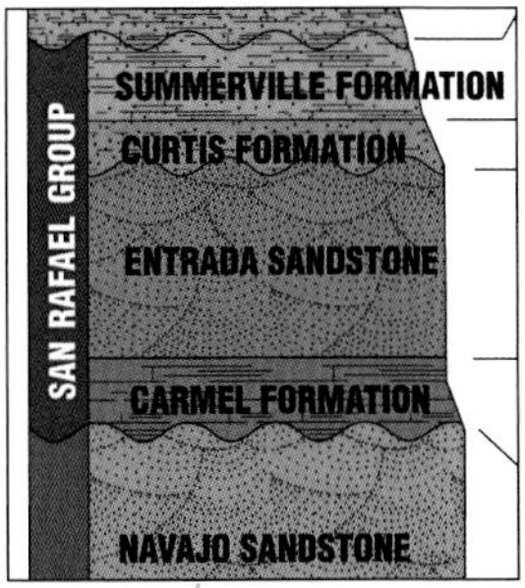

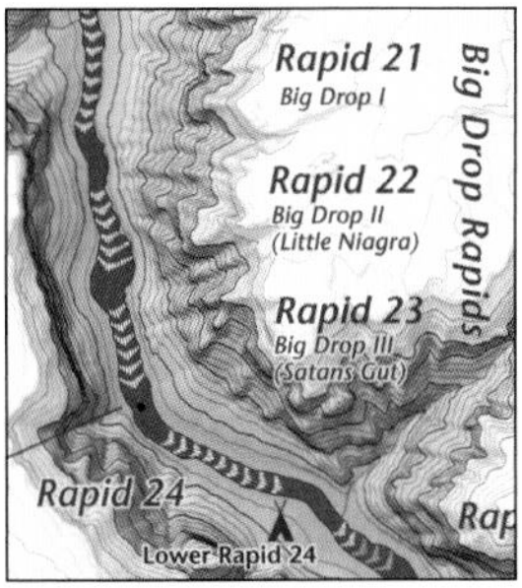

First printing of ALL NEW COLOR EDITION: 2006
First printing of ALL NEW EDITION: 2008

Published by:
WESTWATER BOOKS
A division of Belknap Photographic Services, Inc.
Evergreen, Colorado 80439.

Credits
Design and cartography: Buzz Belknap
Text: Bill Belknap, Loie Belknap Evans; Geology Text: R. J. Johnson
Editor: Jodi Parry Belknap; Managing Editor: Loie Belknap Evans
Assistant Managing Editor: Lynn Evans Peesel; Production Assistant: Richard Hepburn

Manuscript and map review past and present: Otis "Dock" Marston; Bates Wilson; Chad Niehaus, Troy Schnurr, Bureau of Land Management; Kyler Carpenter, Neal Herbert and Steve Young, Canyonlands National Park; Day DeLaHunt; Diane Boyer; John Weisheit.

Special appreciation to: Cline Library Special Collections NAU, John Evans, Steve Wagenseller, and to the late Otis "Dock" Marston for sharing his river research and photographs.

Thanks to: Adventure Bound River Expeditions; Pearl Baker; Glen Baxter; Bego; George Billingsley; Canyon Voyages; Paul and Miki Hasegawa; Dee and Sue Holladay; Holiday River Expeditions; John Wesley Powell River History Museum; the late Earl Leseberg; Moki Mac River Expeditions Inc.; Redtail Aviation; W.L. Rusho; Sheri Griffith River Expeditions; Tag-A-Long Expeditions; Tex's Riverways; Ron Smith; Karen Wattenmaker; Western River Expeditions.

Additional Acknowledgements: Historical information courtesy Colorado Plateau River Guides, an organization dedicated to protecting the rivers of the Colorado Plateau, P.O. Box 344, Moab, UT 84532, 435-259-3598. Railroad historical information from Robert W. McLeod, co-author, *Little Book Cliff Railway,* Lampert and McLeod, Pruett Publishing Company, Boulder, Colorado 1984. Content page photos: Rafting photo courtesy National Park Service - Neal Herbert; Mountain bike photo courtesy Holiday Expeditions - photo by Chris Noble.

Library of Congress Control Number: 2007941228
ISBN-13: 978-0-916370-17-6
ISBN-10: 0-916370-17-8
Printed in China

"Big Drop Three"
Serena Supplee

INDEX MAP

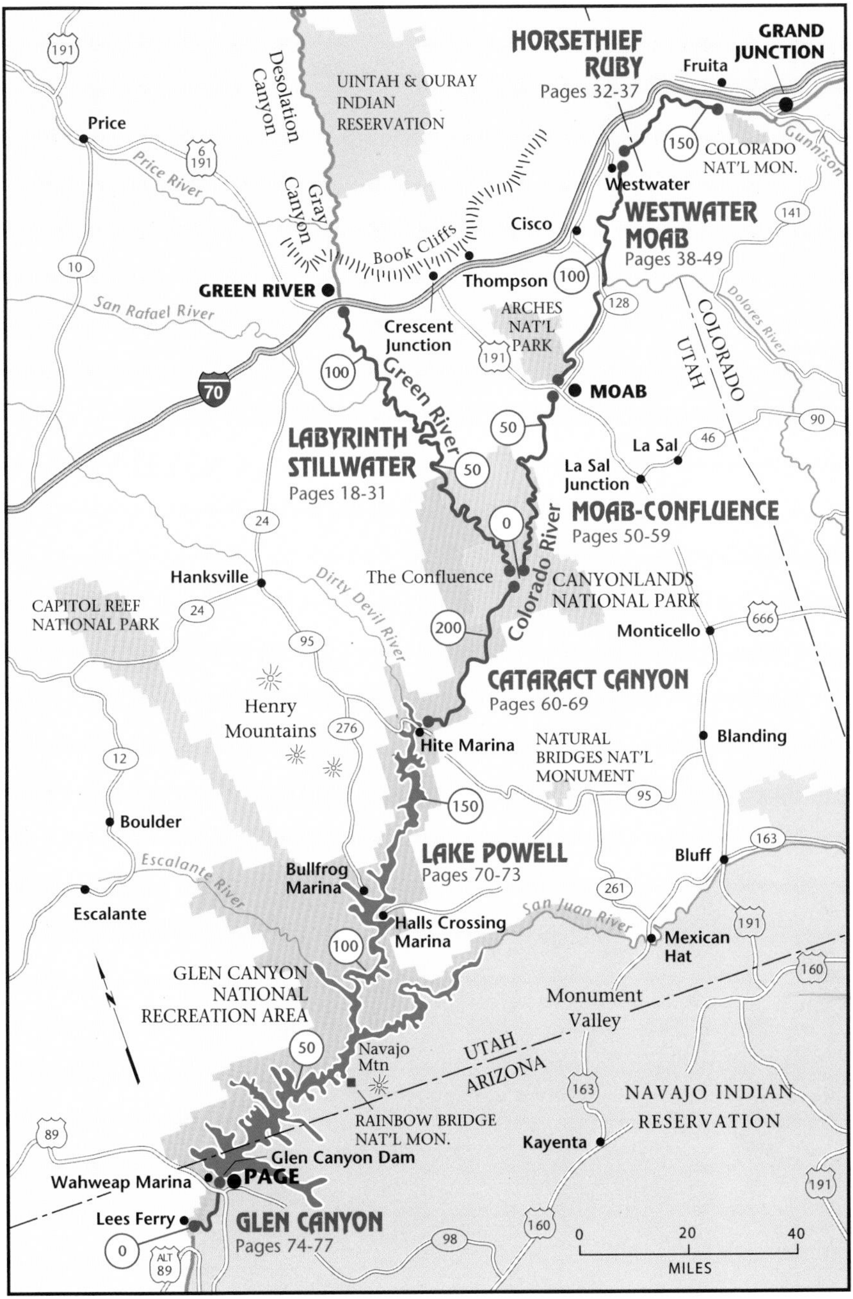
HORSETHIEF
RUBY
Pages 32-37
GRAND
JUNCTION
Fruita
Gunnison
COLORADO
NAT'L MON.
Westwater
WESTWATER
MOAB
Pages 38-49
Cisco
Thompson
Book Cliffs
UINTAH & OURAY
INDIAN
RESERVATION
Desolation
Canyon
Gray
Canyon
Price
Price River
GREEN RIVER
San Rafael River
Crescent
Junction
ARCHES
NAT'L
PARK
MOAB
Green River
Dolores River
COLORADO
UTAH
LABYRINTH
STILLWATER
Pages 18-31
La Sal
La Sal
Junction
MOAB-CONFLUENCE
Pages 50-59
The Confluence
Colorado River
CANYONLANDS
NATIONAL PARK
Hanksville
Dirty Devil River
CAPITOL REEF
NATIONAL PARK
Monticello
CATARACT CANYON
Pages 60-69
Henry
Mountains
Hite Marina
NATURAL
BRIDGES NAT'L
MONUMENT
Blanding
Boulder
Escalante River
Escalante
LAKE POWELL
Pages 70-73
Bullfrog
Marina
Halls Crossing
Marina
Bluff
San Juan River
Mexican
Hat
GLEN CANYON
NATIONAL
RECREATION AREA
Monument
Valley
Navajo
Mtn
UTAH
ARIZONA
RAINBOW BRIDGE
NAT'L MON.
NAVAJO INDIAN
RESERVATION
Kayenta
Glen Canyon Dam
Wahweap Marina
PAGE
Lees Ferry
GLEN CANYON
Pages 74-77
0
20
40
MILES

GEOLOGIC HISTORY OF CANYONLANDS

Text and Diagrams by R. J. Johnson

Surrounded by uplifts and cliffs, Canyonlands is at the heart of the Colorado Plateau. The Plateau is a vast highland with an average elevation of 5,000 feet, incorporating portions of the Four Corners states. Although bound by the geologically complex regions of the Rocky Mountains and Great Basin, it rose with most of its flat-lying strata intact. Yet, in Canyonlands, its folds and faults are at times spectacularly displayed.

Beautiful red rock blankets the Colorado Plateau, and Canyonlands is no exception. More than half of the rock sequence exposed throughout this region is either red, white, or varicolored sandstone or shale, with the remainder commonly being gray or white limestone, gypsum, or conglomerate deposits.

How and where did these beautiful multicolored rocks form? What earth processes were responsible?

Paleozoic Era: Pennsylvanian age rocks (about 300 million years old) are the oldest strata exposed in Canyonlands. During this time the Uncompahgre Uplift, part of the Ancestral Rockies, rose near the Colorado-Utah border. This highland was surrounded

Physiographic Setting of Canyonlands showing the major geologic features. Inset shows the general boundary of the Colorado Plateau.

DIAGRAM BY R. J. JOHNSON/COMPUTER ILLUSTRATION BY KYM L. MILLER

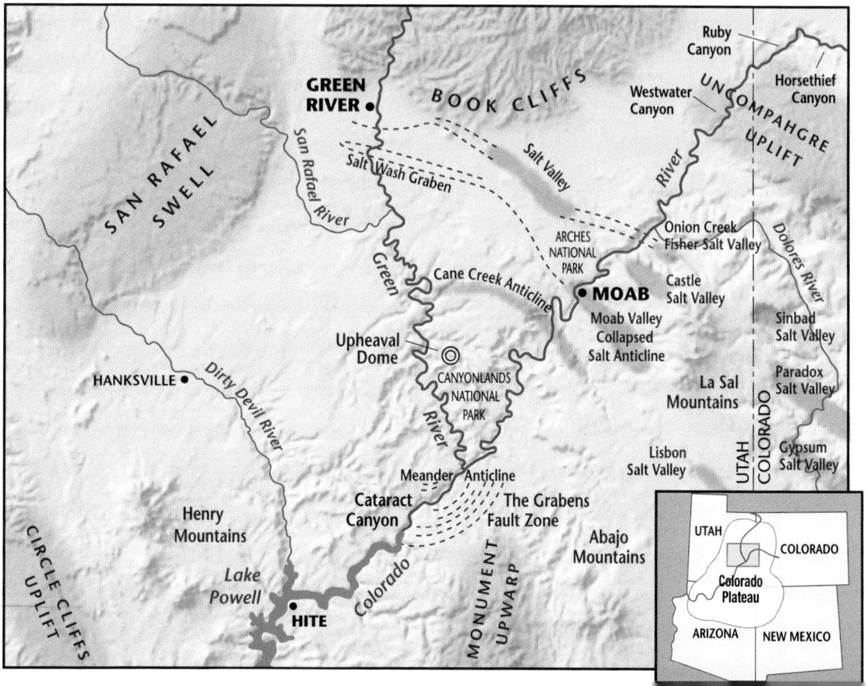

Major Divisions of Geologic Time

(m.y. = millions of years ago)

Archean Eon
4,500 m.y. to 2,500 m.y.

Proterozoic Eon
2,500 m.y. to 570 m.y.

Paleozoic Era
570 m.y. to 240 m.y.

Mesozoic Era
240 m.y. to 65 m.y.

Cenozoic Era
65 m.y. to present

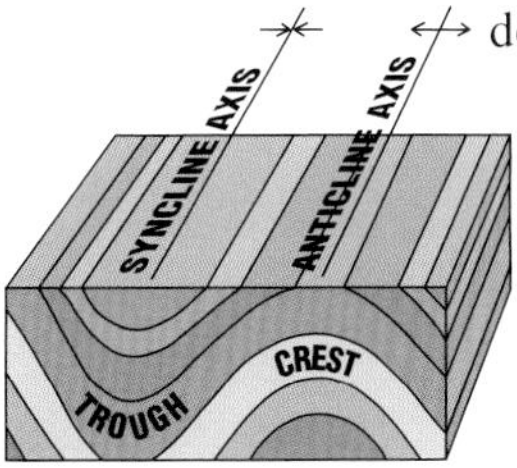

Anticline: upward fold or warp where rocks tilt away from the central axis. After erosion the older rocks are exposed at the core. Anticlines are commonly formed by regional earth movements, but in Canyonlands they mainly form by salt masses bulging into overlying sediments. Separating these upwarps are **Synclines**: downward folds where rocks tilt toward the central axis. After erosion, the younger rocks are exposed at the core.

by basins which began accumulating sediment. The Paradox Basin to the southwest was intermittently cut off and isolated from a nearby ocean. Seawater in this basin evaporated, leaving behind evaporite minerals such as halite (salt), gypsum, and potash. Twenty-nine cycles occurred during this wet/dry period, producing a stack of evaporite minerals thousands of feet thick. These salt beds, later squeezed and deformed by the weight of overlying sediments, helped develop today's salt valleys.

Shallow seas predominated at the end of the Pennsylvanian Period, bringing fossil-rich limestone and shale deposition. At the close of the Paleozoic Era in the Permian Period (260 million years ago) sea levels varied as did the environments of deposition. Thin limestones and red and white sandstones and shales, were deposited in marine, coastal stream, and desert environments.

Mesozoic Era: The Mesozoic Era began with shale, silt, and sand deposition in broad mud flats and stream channels, which today may contain uranium or petrified wood. Often above sea level during the Jurassic and Triassic periods (220 to 175 million years ago), large deserts generated sand dunes, today recognized by cross stratification commonly seen on cliff and slope faces. Throughout the Jurassic and Cretaceous periods (100 million years ago) depositional conditions alternated between shallow seas, rivers, lakes, and deserts. During this time a large dinosaur population roamed the swamps and mud flats. The shales which form the vast badlands topography north of Canyonlands were deposited in relatively placid waters as the Mesozoic Era came to a close.

Cenozoic Era: The land was on the rise from Late Mesozoic to Early Cenozoic time during which large uplifts developed—for example, the Uncompahgre Uplift, Monument Upwarp, San Rafael Swell, and Circle Cliffs Uplift.

Stripping of the sediment cover occurred as small creeks turned into streams, which in turn developed into rivers, and the drainages of the Colorado and Green rivers took shape. Most drainages established their courses by cutting into relatively flat-lying sediment surfaces to create meandering stream patterns. Uplift of the Colorado Plateau began about 15 million years ago, increasing the cutting power of each river. As uplift progressed, the softer, more erosion-prone rock was removed and the harder, or more strongly-bonded rock remained, accounting for such intriguing landforms as the buttes, pinnacles, and spires seen today.

GEOLOGY

CANYONLANDS CROSS SECTION/OBLIQUE VIEW
(Near the Confluence of the Green and Colorado rivers looking northward)

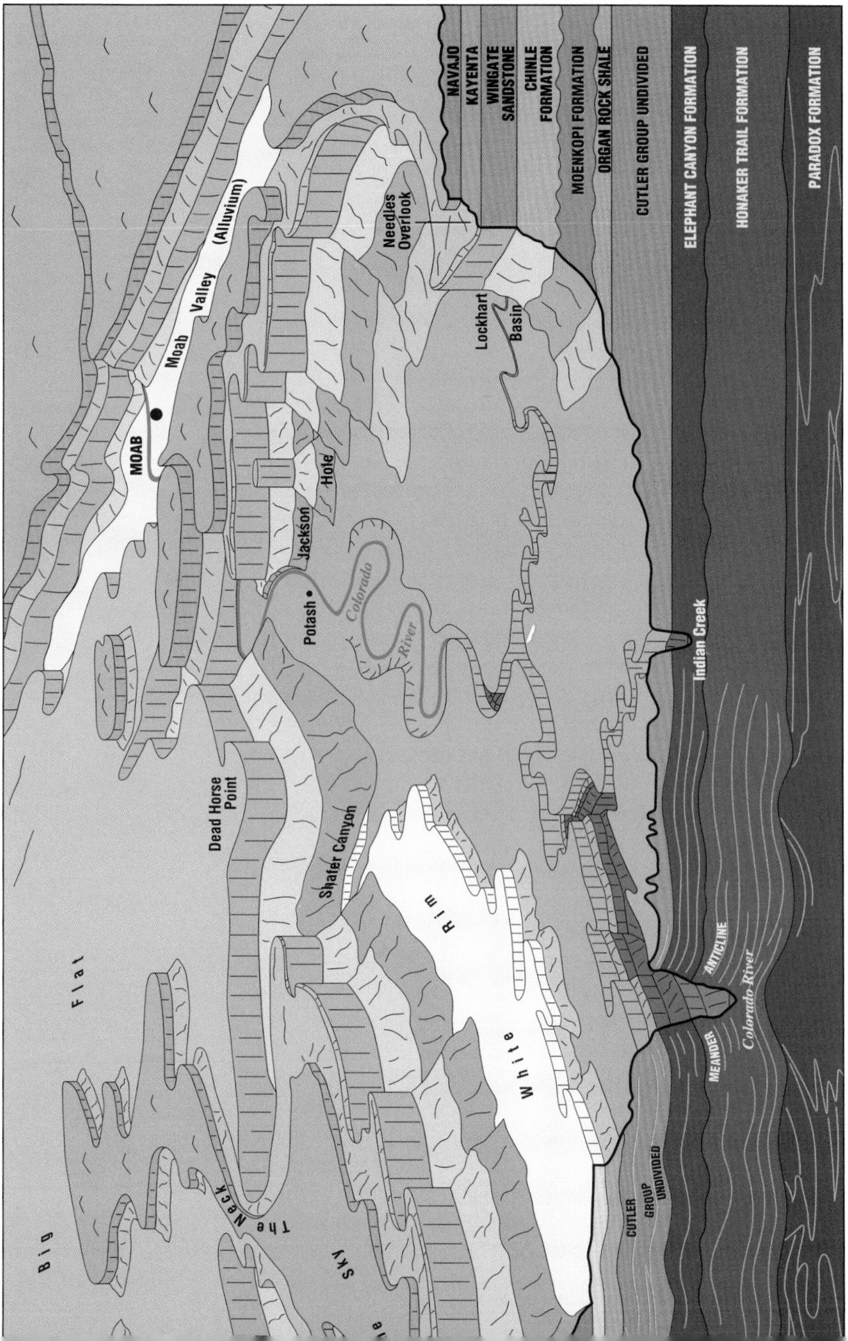

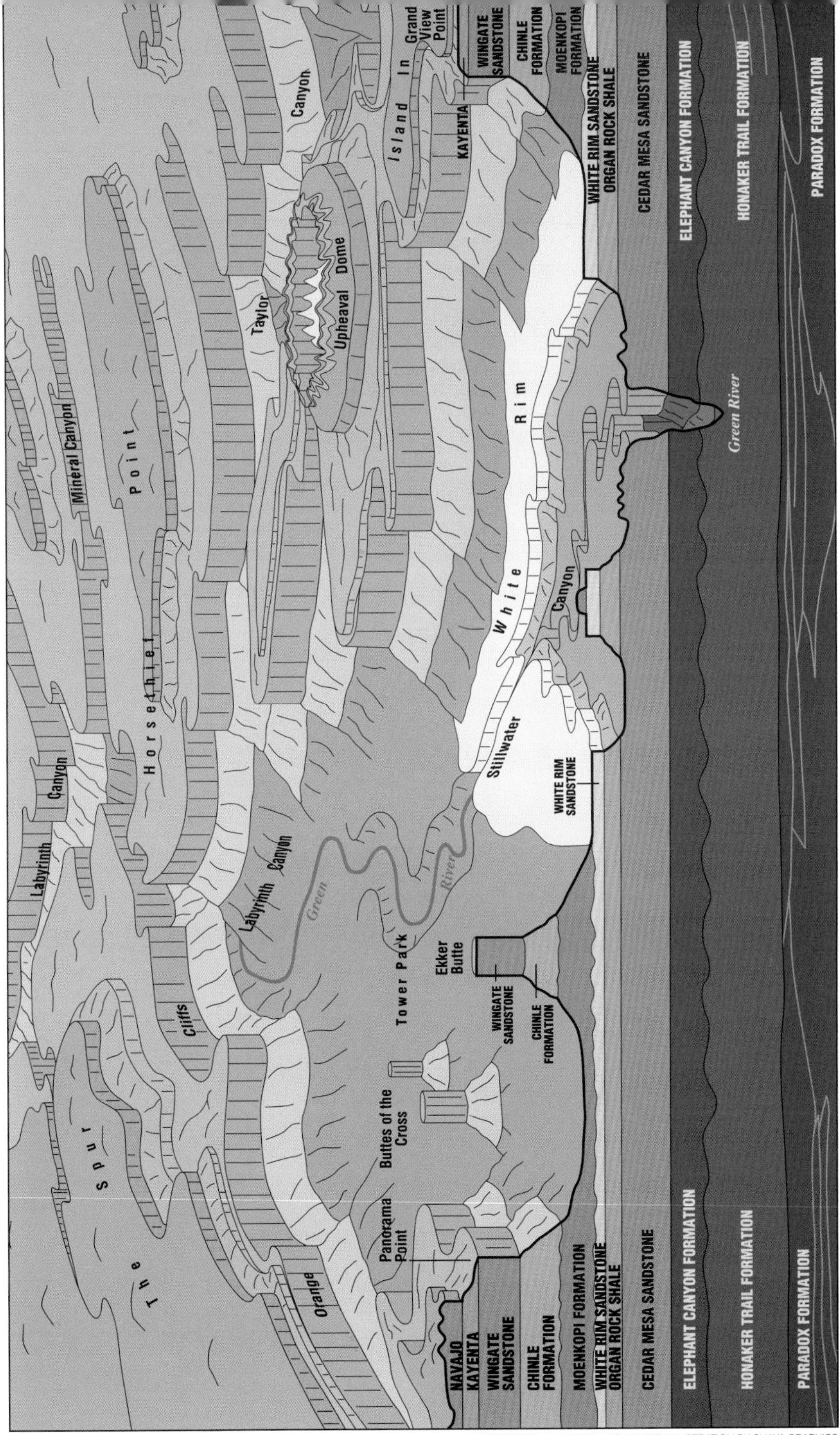

DIAGRAM BY R. J. JOHNSON/COMPUTER ILLUSTRATION BY GUAVA GRAPHICS

SPECIAL GEOLOGIC FEATURES OF CANYONLANDS

UPHEAVAL DOME SATELLITE PHOTO - COURTESY Digital Globe

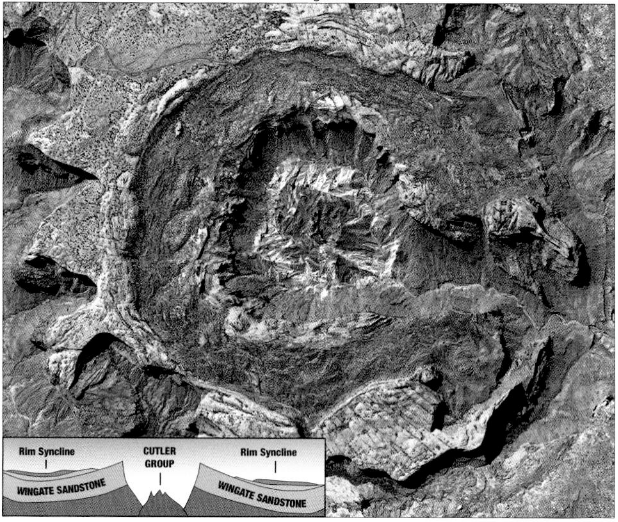

Upheaval Dome: About a mile in diameter and a quarter mile deep, Upheaval Dome (pictured above) is an unexpected feature in the relatively flat-lying sediments of Canyonlands. What forces put a structure like this in such an unlikely place? The presently accepted theory suggests that about 65 million years ago, when Canyonlands was covered by thousands of feet of additional sediment, a meteorite vaporized when it struck the earth. Salts from the underlying Paradox Formation migrated rapidly upward following the circular fracture pattern created by the meteorite impact. An alternative theory suggests a partly extruded salt diapir (dome) was pinched off from its source. Under either theory more recent erosion helped develop the shape of today's Upheaval Dome.

Arches: Arch formation, such as that found in the Entrada Sandstone of Arches National Park, occurs when parallel fractures in rock create a series of freestanding slabs or "fins." Shallow ground water percolating through the fractures slowly dissolves the cement which binds adjacent sand grains. This process weakens the rock along horizontal fractures and bedding planes and undercuts the fin, eventually leaving an arch.

Igneous Intrusive bodies: The mountain ranges of the La Sals, the Henrys, the Abajos, as well as Navajo Mountain, stand well above the relatively flat-lying sediments of the Colorado Plateau. Each mountain was formed by cores of molten igneous rock which pushed upward into overlying sediment as if attempting to pierce the earth's surface. Later exposed by erosion, the upper portions of these underlying mushroom-shaped igneous bodies (laccoliths) appear on some of the mountains' flanks.

Evaporite Minerals: Cycles of flooding and evaporation within closed basins may create a sequence of mineral deposits commonly called bedded salt, which include dolomite, gypsum, anhydrite, halite (salt), and potash.

Salt Valleys: Millions of years of repeated evaporation of a shallow restricted sea (beginning about 300 m.y. ago) accumulated thousands of feet of bedded salts in Canyonlands. After salt deposition ceased, large quantities of sediment continued to accumulate, adding weight over the salt. This added weight squeezed the salt which began to flow horizontally until it was deflected upward after encountering deep-seated fault barriers. Rising toward the surface, it warped the overlying sediment layers. After this 150-million-year long process, circulating ground water began to remove salt from the resulting bulges, collapsing the overlying sediment inward and creating salt valleys. The Colorado River cuts through the collapsed salt anticline of the Moab/Spanish Valley and flows near the edges of other salt valleys in the region, including Salt, Castle, and Onion Creek/Fisher.

Potash: Downstream from Moab, potash is mined by injecting Colorado River water underground, letting the water become saturated with salts, and then pumping it to the surface where it evaporates, forming crystals. Potash is used as fertilizer.

Uranium: During the 1950s prospectors searched for uranium deposited along ancient meandering stream channels in the Morrison and Chinle formations. The Mi Vida uranium mine south of Moab had an original estimated value of $72 million and helped swell Moab's population. Eventually oversupply and foreign competition decreased the demand for the mineral, bringing an abrupt end to the uranium boom in the 1970s.

Oil: Abandoned wells are remnants of limited oil and gas exploration in Canyonlands. Pennsylvanian and Mississippian rocks host the few still successful oil fields in the region. Gas exploration has produced meager results.

Rock Color: Trace amounts of minerals (usually less than one percent) are commonly the cause of color in rocks. If a rock is red its color is probably caused by iron oxide. The chemistry of iron forms various hues of black, green, yellow, and red. Organic matter or a lack of oxygen during deposition can develop colors of black (coal) or gray (shale or limestone). Volcanic ash layers may be gray, green, white, or purple. Manganese can color rocks black, brown, red, or purple. White sandstones or evaporites are usually free of trace minerals and other impurities. Surface stains may sometimes be misleading, though, and hide the true rock color beneath.

Desert Varnish: A lustrous, smooth patina of iron or manganese oxides, or clay minerals of black, brown, tan, or orange, desert varnish is thought to be derived from the interaction of airborne dust and microscopic plants upon an exposed rock under moist conditions. It may coat many different rock surfaces. Look for it on the massive vertical cliffs of Wingate Sandstone, the horizontal platform atop the White Rim Sandstone, or on loose, pebbly or blocky surface material in other areas of Canyonlands.

DIAGRAM BY R. J. JOHNSON

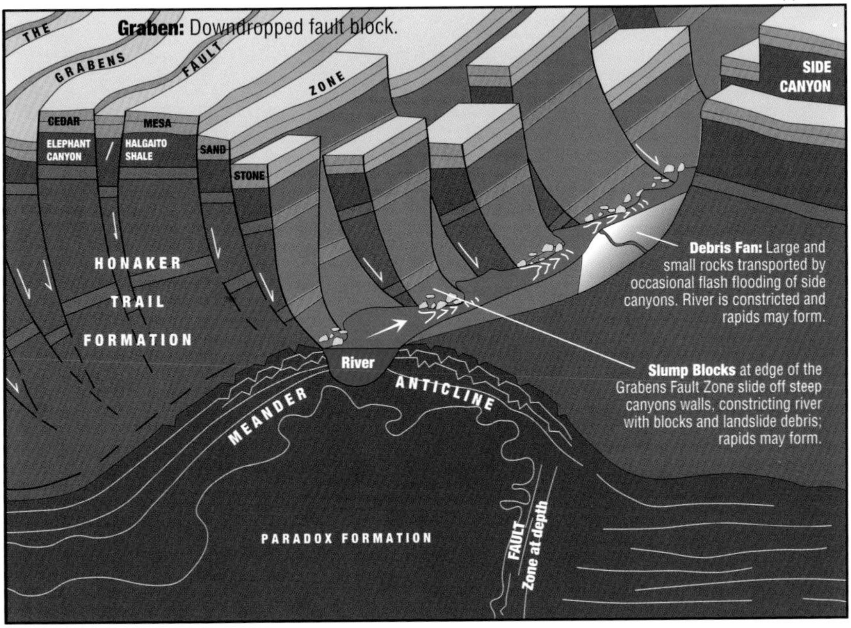

Graben: Downdropped fault block.
THE GRABENS FAULT ZONE
CEDAR MESA SANDSTONE
ELEPHANT CANYON
HALGAITO SHALE
SIDE CANYON
HONAKER TRAIL FORMATION
River
MEANDER ANTICLINE
PARADOX FORMATION
FAULT Zone at depth
Debris Fan: Large and small rocks transported by occasional flash flooding of side canyons. River is constricted and rapids may form.
Slump Blocks at edge of the Grabens Fault Zone slide off steep canyons walls, constricting river with blocks and landslide debris; rapids may form.

Cataract Canyon: Cutaway view showing ongoing geologic processes and underlying physical structure in Cataract, including Grabens Fault Zone (upper left), river flowing along Meander Anticline, and two ways rapids are formed (see Debris Fan and Slump Blocks on diagram). Two theories for the Meander Anticline formation are: 1) squeezed by surrounding weight of canyon walls, salt flowed below the downcutting river, arching the strata beneath the existing riverbed; and 2) salt flow impeded at depth deflected upward, arching and fracturing the overlying strata, allowing the river to cut into and follow the weakened pathway. In either case faulting occurs in the Grabens Fault Zone as rocks atop the underlying salt slide toward the canyon.

GEOLOGY

ROCK SEQUENCE OF CANYONLANDS

The sequence below shows successive rock layers in Canyonlands along the Green and Colorado rivers with oldest at the bottom and youngest at the top. *Italics* indicate dominant rock type(s).

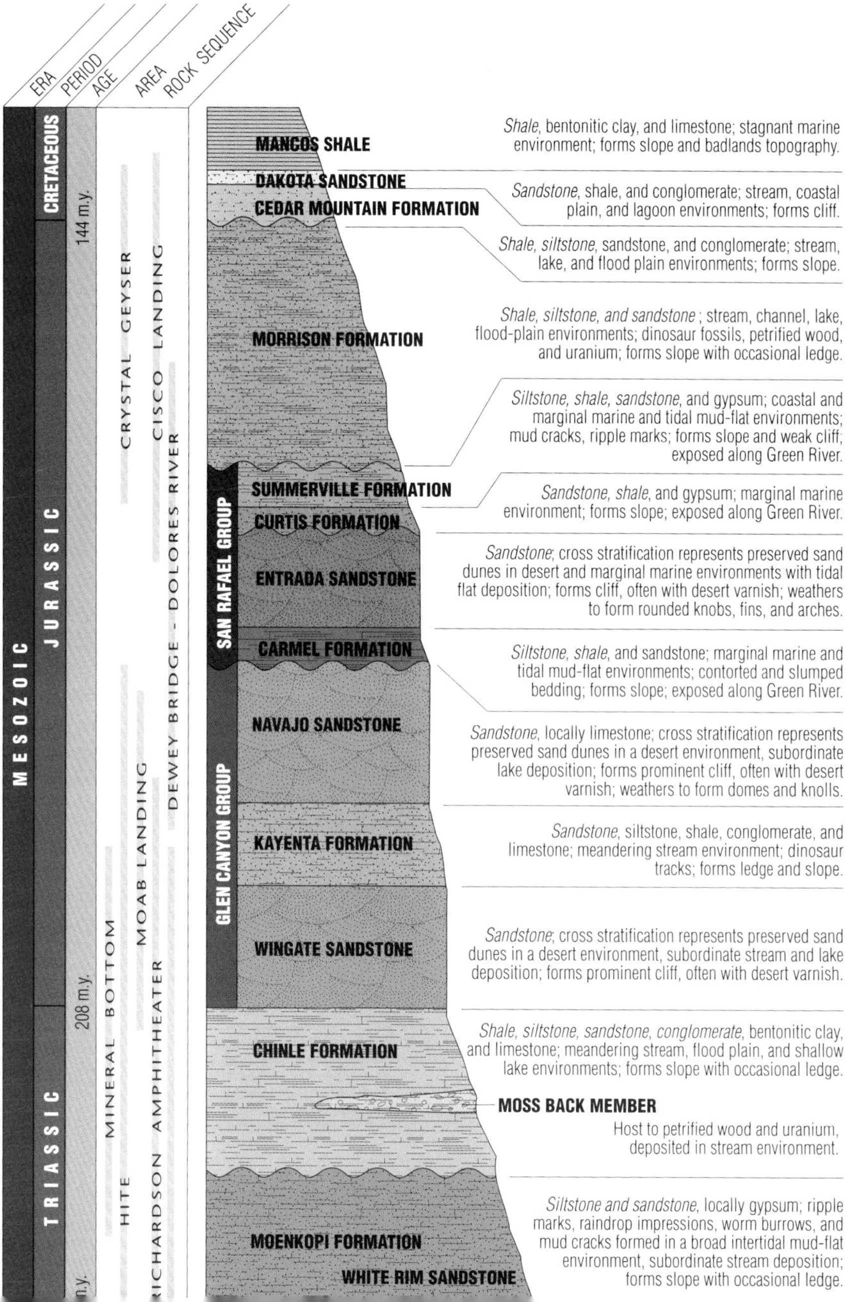
ERA
PERIOD
AGE
AREA
ROCK SEQUENCE
MESOZOIC
CRETACEOUS
JURASSIC
TRIASSIC
144 m.y.
208 m.y.
m.y.
CRYSTAL GEYSER
CISCO LANDING
DEWEY BRIDGE - DOLORES RIVER
MOAB LANDING
MINERAL BOTTOM
HITE
RICHARDSON AMPHITHEATER
SAN RAFAEL GROUP
GLEN CANYON GROUP
MANCOS SHALE
Shale, bentonitic clay, and limestone; stagnant marine environment; forms slope and badlands topography.
DAKOTA SANDSTONE
Sandstone, shale, and conglomerate; stream, coastal plain, and lagoon environments; forms cliff.
CEDAR MOUNTAIN FORMATION
Shale, siltstone, sandstone, and conglomerate; stream, lake, and flood plain environments; forms slope.
MORRISON FORMATION
Shale, siltstone, and sandstone ; stream, channel, lake, flood-plain environments; dinosaur fossils, petrified wood, and uranium; forms slope with occasional ledge.
Siltstone, shale, sandstone, and gypsum; coastal and marginal marine and tidal mud-flat environments; mud cracks, ripple marks; forms slope and weak cliff; exposed along Green River.
SUMMERVILLE FORMATION
Sandstone, shale, and gypsum; marginal marine environment; forms slope; exposed along Green River.
CURTIS FORMATION
ENTRADA SANDSTONE
Sandstone; cross stratification represents preserved sand dunes in desert and marginal marine environments with tidal flat deposition; forms cliff, often with desert varnish; weathers to form rounded knobs, fins, and arches.
CARMEL FORMATION
Siltstone, shale, and sandstone; marginal marine and tidal mud-flat environments; contorted and slumped bedding; forms slope; exposed along Green River.
NAVAJO SANDSTONE
Sandstone, locally limestone; cross stratification represents preserved sand dunes in a desert environment, subordinate lake deposition; forms prominent cliff, often with desert varnish; weathers to form domes and knolls.
KAYENTA FORMATION
Sandstone, siltstone, shale, conglomerate, and limestone; meandering stream environment; dinosaur tracks; forms ledge and slope.
WINGATE SANDSTONE
Sandstone; cross stratification represents preserved sand dunes in a desert environment, subordinate stream and lake deposition; forms prominent cliff, often with desert varnish.
CHINLE FORMATION
Shale, siltstone, sandstone, conglomerate, bentonitic clay, and limestone; meandering stream, flood plain, and shallow lake environments; forms slope with occasional ledge.
MOSS BACK MEMBER
Host to petrified wood and uranium, deposited in stream environment.
MOENKOPI FORMATION
Siltstone and sandstone, locally gypsum; ripple marks, raindrop impressions, worm burrows, and mud cracks formed in a broad intertidal mud-flat environment, subordinate stream deposition; forms slope with occasional ledge.
WHITE RIM SANDSTONE

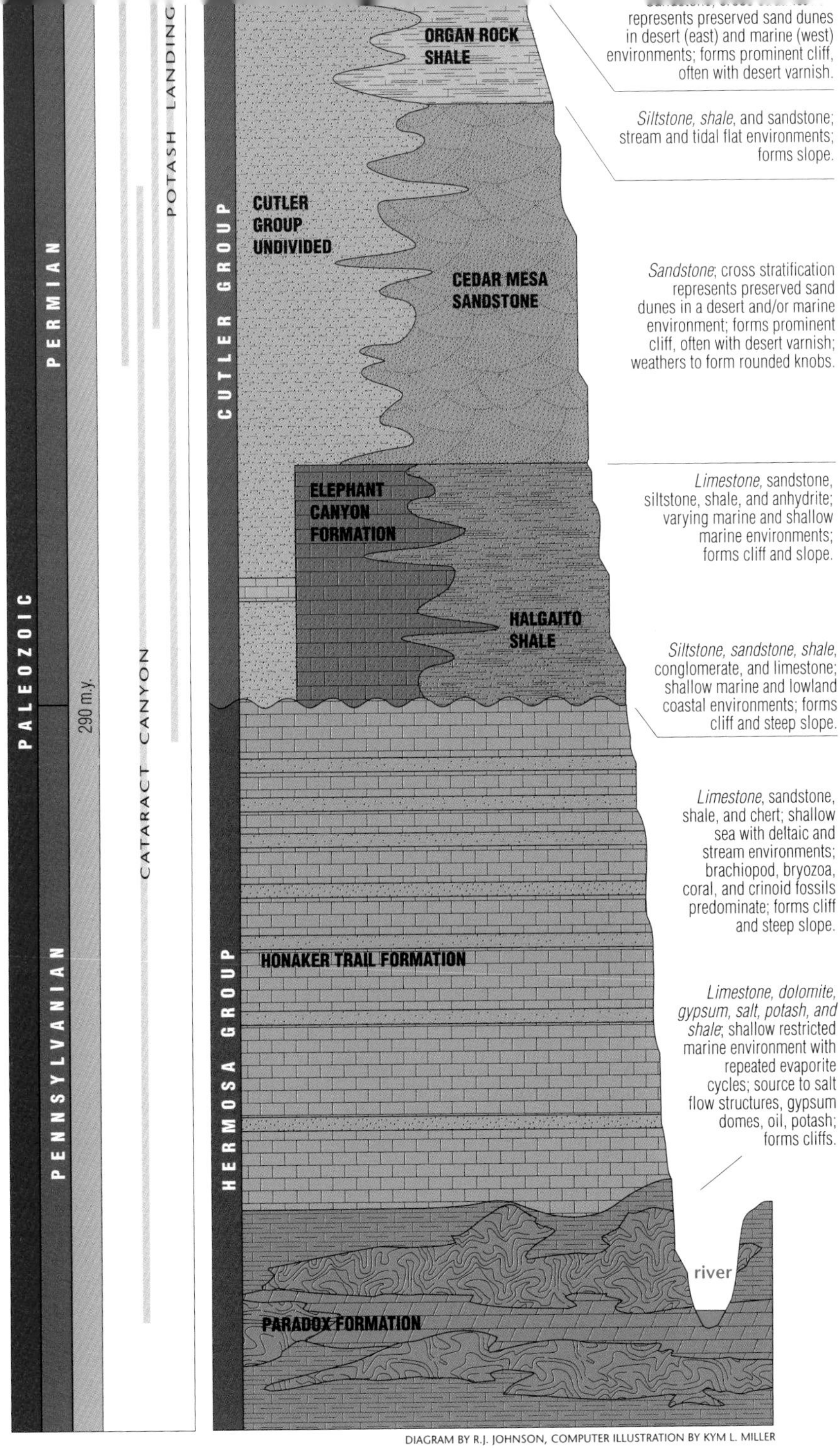

PALEOZOIC
PERMIAN
PENNSYLVANIAN
290 m.y.
CATARACT CANYON
POTASH LANDING
CUTLER GROUP
HERMOSA GROUP
ORGAN ROCK SHALE
CUTLER GROUP UNDIVIDED
CEDAR MESA SANDSTONE
ELEPHANT CANYON FORMATION
HALGAITO SHALE
HONAKER TRAIL FORMATION
PARADOX FORMATION
river
represents preserved sand dunes in desert (east) and marine (west) environments; forms prominent cliff, often with desert varnish.
Siltstone, shale, and sandstone; stream and tidal flat environments; forms slope.
Sandstone; cross stratification represents preserved sand dunes in a desert and/or marine environment; forms prominent cliff, often with desert varnish; weathers to form rounded knobs.
Limestone, sandstone, siltstone, shale, and anhydrite; varying marine and shallow marine environments; forms cliff and slope.
Siltstone, sandstone, shale, conglomerate, and limestone; shallow marine and lowland coastal environments; forms cliff and steep slope.
Limestone, sandstone, shale, and chert; shallow sea with deltaic and stream environments; brachiopod, bryozoa, coral, and crinoid fossils predominate; forms cliff and steep slope.
Limestone, dolomite, gypsum, salt, potash, and shale; shallow restricted marine environment with repeated evaporite cycles; source to salt flow structures, gypsum domes, oil, potash; forms cliffs.

DIAGRAM BY R.J. JOHNSON, COMPUTER ILLUSTRATION BY KYM L. MILLER

GEOLOGIC HISTORY OF WESTWATER AND RUBY CANYONS

As you float through Westwater Canyon or Black Rocks in Ruby Canyon, look closely at the rock exposed in the inner gorge—it is 1.7 billion years old. Composed of crystal-rich gneiss and granite, it has been folded and fractured, evidence of its complex history. Lying directly upon these ancient crystalline rocks and forming the upper canyon walls are Mesozoic age (220 million year old) sediments. That means there is a 1.5 billion year gap in the rock record.

What happened to the missing rock and what created this nonconformable surface?

During development of the Ancestral Rockies about 300 million years ago, deep-seated faults surrounding the Uncompahgre Uplift were reactivated. Movement along these faults uplifted this region, creating scenes of earth disturbance not evident for more than one billion years. As this highland block eroded, debris accumulated in the nearby Paradox Basin to the south, and in Eagle Basin to the north. In addition, thousands of feet of evaporite minerals were also deposited in these basins. Uplift slowed 260 million years ago during the Permian Period, after which Mesozoic age sediment covered this eroded mountain of Proterozoic rock and created the nonconformable surface seen today.

What happened to cause the river to cut through these ancient, resistant rocks of the Uncompahgre and what shaped these canyons?

Renewed uplift during Late Mesozoic and Early Cenozoic times, from 70 to 60 million years ago, pushed the old Uncompahgre Uplift further upward; later, in Middle Cenozoic time, the vast Colorado Plateau began to rise and the Colorado River started to define its course. Meanders were preserved as the river cut through the relatively flat-lying sediments of the elevated Plateau, and the ancient buried Uncompahgre was cut as the river sliced deeper, establishing its present course through these canyons.

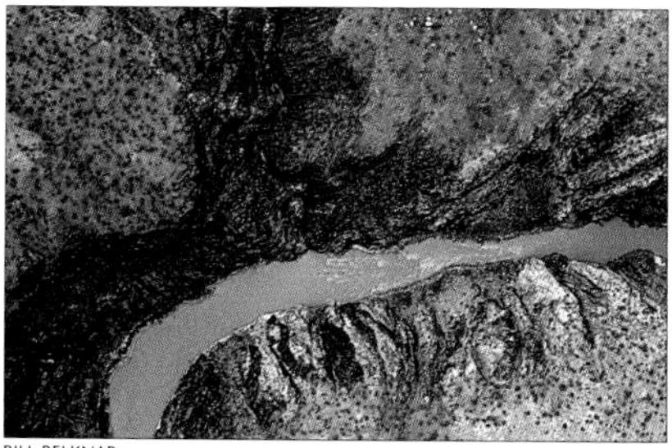
BILL BELKNAP

1.7 Billion Year Old Rocks form inner gorge at Marble Canyon Rapid.

How Rocks are Formed

Igneous Rocks are cooled from a molten state and crystallize. Examples are granite, basalt, pegmatite.

Sedimentary Rocks are deposited as particles in oceans and lakes, or by streams and wind. Examples are limestone, sandstone, shale.

Metamorphic Rocks are changed from a pre-existing rock type by heat, pressure, and chemical activity over time. Examples are marble from limestone, quartzite from sandstone, schist and gneiss from various parent rocks.

Nonconformity Type of unconformity (an erosional surface representing a "gap" in the geologic record and succession of rocks) where stratified rocks rest upon unstratified rocks. For example: sandstone or shale deposition on the erosional surface of granitic or metamorphic rocks.

ROCK SEQUENCE OF HORSETHIEF, RUBY, AND WESTWATER CANYONS

The sequence below shows successive rock layers in Horsethief, Ruby, and Westwater Canyons along the Colorado River with oldest at the bottom and youngest at the top. *Italics* indicate dominant rock type(s).

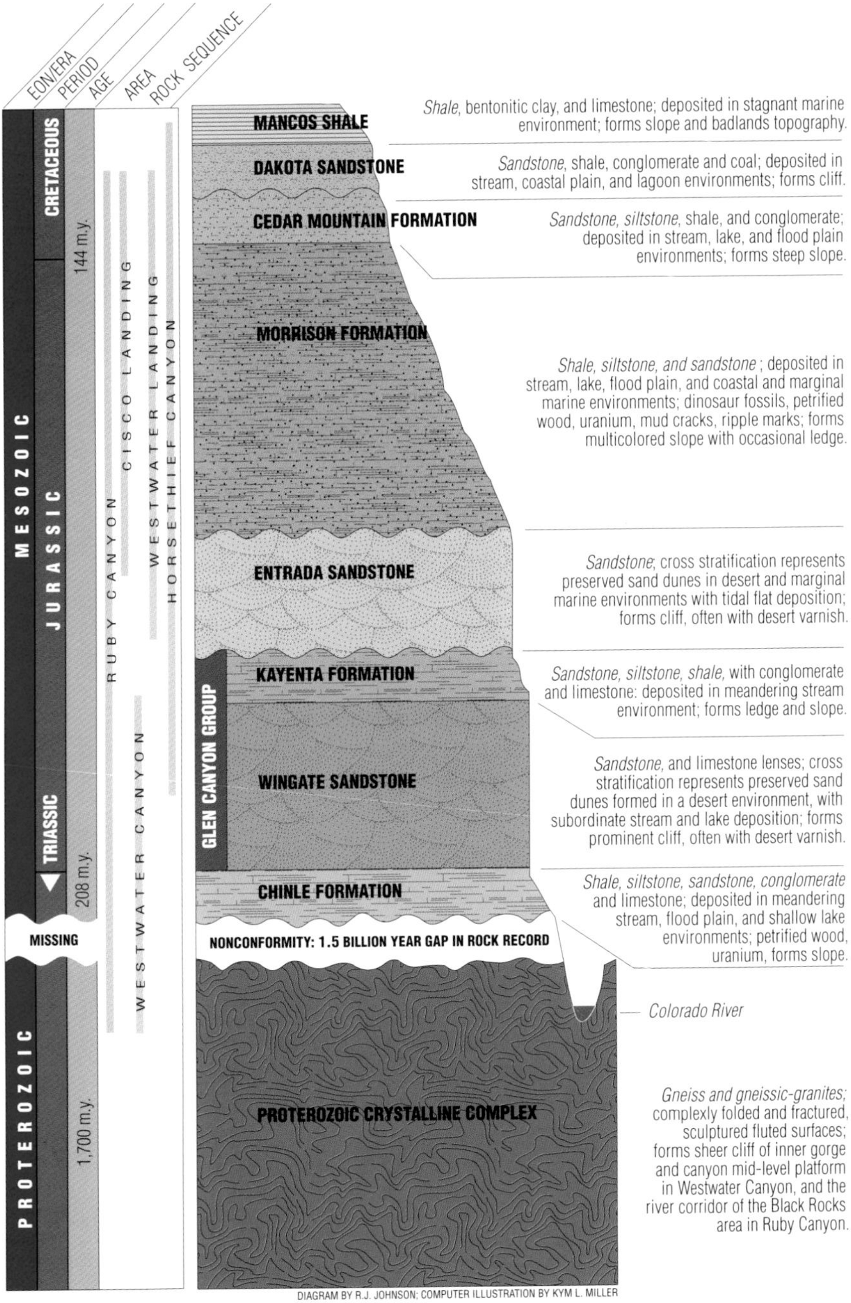
EON/ERA
PERIOD
AGE
AREA
ROCK SEQUENCE
MESOZOIC
PROTEROZOIC
CRETACEOUS
JURASSIC
TRIASSIC
MISSING
144 m.y.
208 m.y.
1,700 m.y.
RUBY CANYON
CISCO LANDING
WESTWATER LANDING
HORSETHIEF CANYON
WESTWATER CANYON
GLEN CANYON GROUP
MANCOS SHALE
Shale, bentonitic clay, and limestone; deposited in stagnant marine environment; forms slope and badlands topography.
DAKOTA SANDSTONE
Sandstone, shale, conglomerate and coal; deposited in stream, coastal plain, and lagoon environments; forms cliff.
CEDAR MOUNTAIN FORMATION
Sandstone, siltstone, shale, and conglomerate; deposited in stream, lake, and flood plain environments; forms steep slope.
MORRISON FORMATION
Shale, siltstone, and sandstone; deposited in stream, lake, flood plain, and coastal and marginal marine environments; dinosaur fossils, petrified wood, uranium, mud cracks, ripple marks; forms multicolored slope with occasional ledge.
ENTRADA SANDSTONE
Sandstone; cross stratification represents preserved sand dunes in desert and marginal marine environments with tidal flat deposition; forms cliff, often with desert varnish.
KAYENTA FORMATION
Sandstone, siltstone, shale, with conglomerate and limestone: deposited in meandering stream environment; forms ledge and slope.
WINGATE SANDSTONE
Sandstone, and limestone lenses; cross stratification represents preserved sand dunes formed in a desert environment, with subordinate stream and lake deposition; forms prominent cliff, often with desert varnish.
CHINLE FORMATION
Shale, siltstone, sandstone, conglomerate and limestone; deposited in meandering stream, flood plain, and shallow lake environments; petrified wood, uranium, forms slope.
NONCONFORMITY: 1.5 BILLION YEAR GAP IN ROCK RECORD
Colorado River
PROTEROZOIC CRYSTALLINE COMPLEX
Gneiss and gneissic-granites; complexly folded and fractured, sculptured fluted surfaces; forms sheer cliff of inner gorge and canyon mid-level platform in Westwater Canyon, and the river corridor of the Black Rocks area in Ruby Canyon.

DIAGRAM BY R.J. JOHNSON; COMPUTER ILLUSTRATION BY KYM L. MILLER

"HARSH, FRAGILE, STARK, BEAUTIFUL"

M. WOODBRIDGE WILLIAMS

Bates Wilson

Whether you're craning your neck to spot it from a jetliner at 30,000 feet, or watching expectantly around the next bend as you cruise downriver, there's a universal fascination about seeing The Confluence—the coming together of the Green and Colorado Rivers—at the heart of Canyonlands. From Indian and outlaw days until the early 1960s the improbable landscape around The Confluence was virtually a no man's-land: remote, little known, and criss-crossed infrequently by ranchers and prospectors.

When Congress established Canyonlands National Park in 1964, Bates Wilson, who knew its far-flung features perhaps better than anyone, became its first superintendent. For years while in charge of nearby Arches National Monument he had worked tirelessly to gain for his beloved Canyonlands country the recognition and status it deserved.

"No words, nor even pictures, can describe the beauty and grandeur of Canyonlands National Park," he once wrote. "Nor can they adequately convey the wonder and sense of mystery that give it dimension and meaning. Harsh and fragile, stark and beautiful—you have to see it to believe it. And even then you may go away with the awesome feeling that its secrets have escaped you, and no matter where you go, its charm will forever tug on you like a magnet."

"No words, nor even pictures, can describe the beauty and grandeur of Canyonlands National Park."

Bates Wilson

The Green and Colorado rivers have long been the easy routes through this twisted terrain, providing food and drink as well as a way. In the spring of 1836 Denis Julien, a French trapper, recorded the first trip along the rivers–apparently heading upstream.

The Utah towns of Green River and Moab grew as the rivers became better known and more traveled. Both have been the starting points for countless voyages—some notable, a few tragic.

When Major John Wesley Powell's pioneering expedition drifted past the site of Green River on July 13, 1869, they noted only an Indian crossing with crude rafts floating alongside the bank. But 20 years later when the ill-fated Brown-Stanton expedition shoved off on May 25, 1889, the Rio Grande Western Railroad had bridged the river and a town of 50 inhabitants had sprung up.

BILL BELKNAP

In 1855 the Mormons who first settled Moab stayed only five months before Indians drove them out; 22 years later in 1877 the community was permanently settled. Before 1900, steamboats occasionally plied the rivers; soon gasoline-powered launches began hauling supplies and people to ranches, mines, and even to a damsite drilling operation at The Confluence. Cattle and sheep were economic mainstays until the uranium boom put Moab on the map in the 1950s, and Texas Gulf Sulphur's potash mine began tapping the thick underlying salt deposits in the early 1960s.

The Confluence
Green River (upper middle) enters Colorado River (once called the Grand).

The Colorado River above The Confluence was called the Grand River until Congress, yielding to pressure from the state of Colorado, changed its name officially in 1921.

From Major Powell's 1869 trip to the mid-1940s, few expeditions, perhaps 25 in all, traversed Cataract Canyon. Then, when cheap war surplus river gear became available—life rafts, assault boats, bridge pontoons, and waterproof bags—fastwater traffic increased dramatically.

Before upstream travel through the rapids was outlawed, William K. Somerville of Lakewood, Colorado, drove the first boat up Cataract Canyon. He piloted a 19-foot Buehler jet, the *Daredevil,* from Hite to Moab in July 1965.

Now all travel through Cataract Canyon is regulated by Canyonlands National Park. A number of commercial outfitters are authorized to carry passengers down the rapids, and private permits are issued if applicants can satisfy the requirements for river experience, craft, and equipment.

BILL BELKNAP

Friendship Cruise at The Slide
For years, the towns of Moab and Green River co-hosted this unique Memorial Day event with as many as 500 pleasure craft making the 184-mile run down the Green to the Confluence and back up the Colorado.

UTAH'S PLAYGROUND

R. J. JOHNSON

John Wesley Powell River History Museum in Green River, Utah, features replicas of historical boats, a River Runners Hall of Fame, and a bas-relief mural depicting Powell's legendary voyage.

The Park Service also requires permits between Moab and The Confluence on the Colorado and for Labyrinth and Stillwater canyons on the Green.

The relatively calm stretches above The Confluence, particularly on the Green, are ideal for canoeing. Spring and fall offer moderate temperatures and lower water suitable for camping on exposed sandbars. Outfitters are available to help with car shuttle services or jet boat transportation of people and canoes back upriver. No matter whether you ride Cataract Canyon's tumultuous rapids, or quietly drift on an exquisite stretch of the Green or Colorado, it will be an experience you'll never forget.

Years after his arduous voyages to survey a railroad down the Colorado, Robert Brewster Stanton wrote, "I would defy anyone to make a journey by boat through those still, weird chasms, and down that yet mysterious river, and not be brought under their influence."

For private permit information, a list of outfitters and the varied services they offer, or other recreational opportunities in the Canyonlands area, contact: National Park Service, Moab, Utah (435) 259-7164, or check website at www.nps.gov/cany/, or Moab Visitor Information at (435) 259-8825 or 1-800-635-6622 or website: www.Discovermoab.com. For BLM information contact: BLM, Moab, Utah, (435) 259-2100 or http://www.ut.blm.gov/Recreation/recriverrunning.html.

4-Wheeling is a popular way to gain access to some of Canyonland's unique land features. Contact the National Park Service for outfitter information and areas suitable for 4-wheel drive vehicles.

TAG-A-LONG EXPEDITIONS

Mountain Bikers enjoy a variety of terrain in Canyonlands, including slickrock.

HOLIDAY EXPEDITIONS - PHOTO BY CHRIS NOBLE

USING YOUR RIVER GUIDE

John Wesley Powell

Powell Report. This notation indicates condensed quotations from *Exploration of the Colorado River of the West and its Tributaries Explored in 1869, 1870, 1871, and 1872* by John Wesley Powell, U.S. Government Printing Office, 1875.

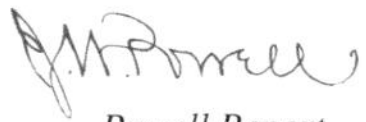

Powell Report

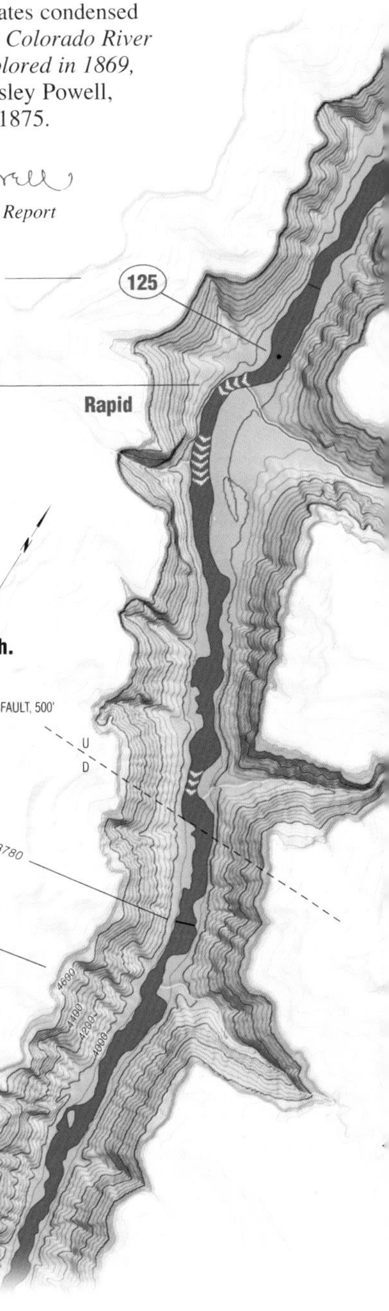

River miles are numbered upriver from Mile 0 at Lees Ferry to The Confluence, then up both the Green and the Colorado starting with another Mile 0 at The Confluence.

Rapids are indicated by breaks in river.

River Maps are based on U.S. Geological Survey *Plan and Profile of Colorado River, Lees Ferry, Arizona, to Mouth of Green River, Utah; San Juan River, Mouth to Chinle Creek, Utah: and Certain Tributaries;* and current USGS seven and one-half minute series quadrangle maps, and USGS digital elevation models (DEM's).

Geologic faults are stress-caused displacement zones in Earth's crust; U (up), D (down), and numbers indicate direction and approximate displacement.

River elevations shown in Cataract Canyon are measured above sea level.

Contours are lines of constant elevation. Contour interval in Cataract Canyon is 50 feet. Heavy contour line is 200. All other map page intervals are 25 feet with heavy contour line at 100 feet. Lines close together indicate steep walls.

IMPORTANT: River channels change frequently, sometimes within a few hours.Rocks, sandbars, or other obstructions may suddenly be laid in or washed away. Due to possible changes subsequent to publication, or inadvertent errors in source materials, WESTWATER BOOKS cannot be responsible for inaccuracies or omissions in CANYONLANDS RIVER GUIDE.

LABYRINTH/STILLWATER

Once you've traveled this 120-mile stretch you'll remember it as ever-deepening canyons of whites and grays and yellows and browns, tastefully accented with just enough red buttes, mesas, and spires to be visually exciting.

It's the longest smooth-water piece of the Green, although shallow riffles and small waves show up at certain river levels in the first 20 miles below the town of Green River.

Permits are required for Labyrinth Canyon, (town of Green River to Mineral Bottom), and may be obtained at Green River State Park and the John Wesley Powell River History Museum in Green River, BLM headquarters in Price or Moab, or at Canyonlands National Park Headquarters in Moab. For latest information check the BLM website at: www.ut.blm.gov/Recreation/recriverrunning.html. You can also call (435) 636-3600. The National Park Service requires a boating permit for Stillwater Canyon (Mineral Bottom to the Confluence) and for continuing through Cataract Canyon. For information about permits, shuttle, and jet boat pick-up service, contact: NPS, 2282 S. West Resource Blvd., Moab, UT 84532 (435) 259-7164 or www.nps.gov/cany/.

Above photo: Buttes of the Cross
BY BILL BELKNAP

RIVER FLOW INFORMATION
CALL: 801-539-1311 or go to www.cbrfc.noaa.gov/

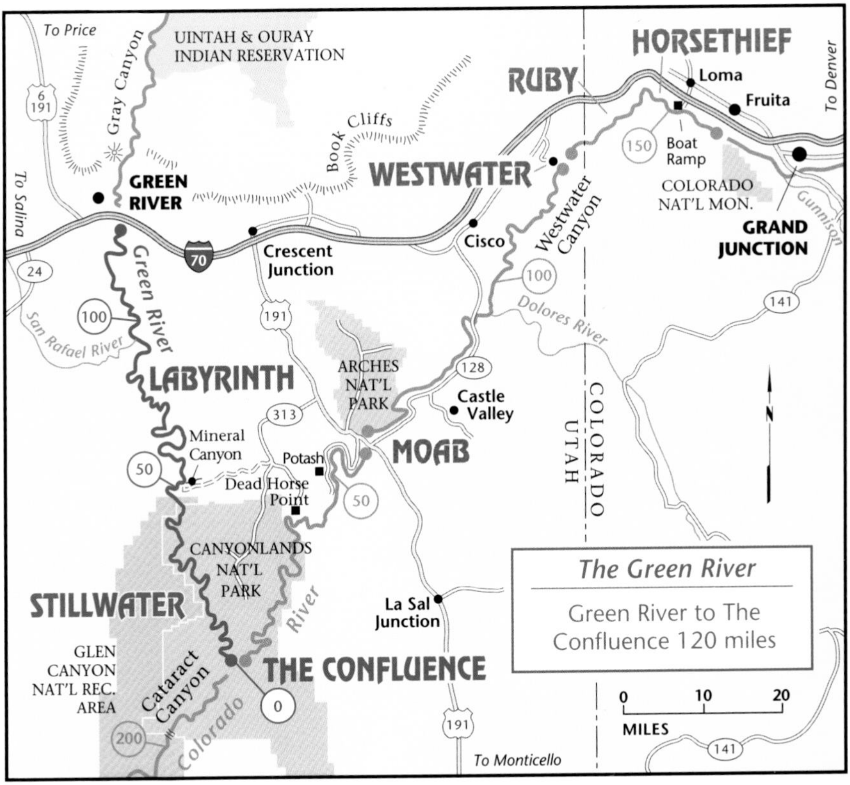

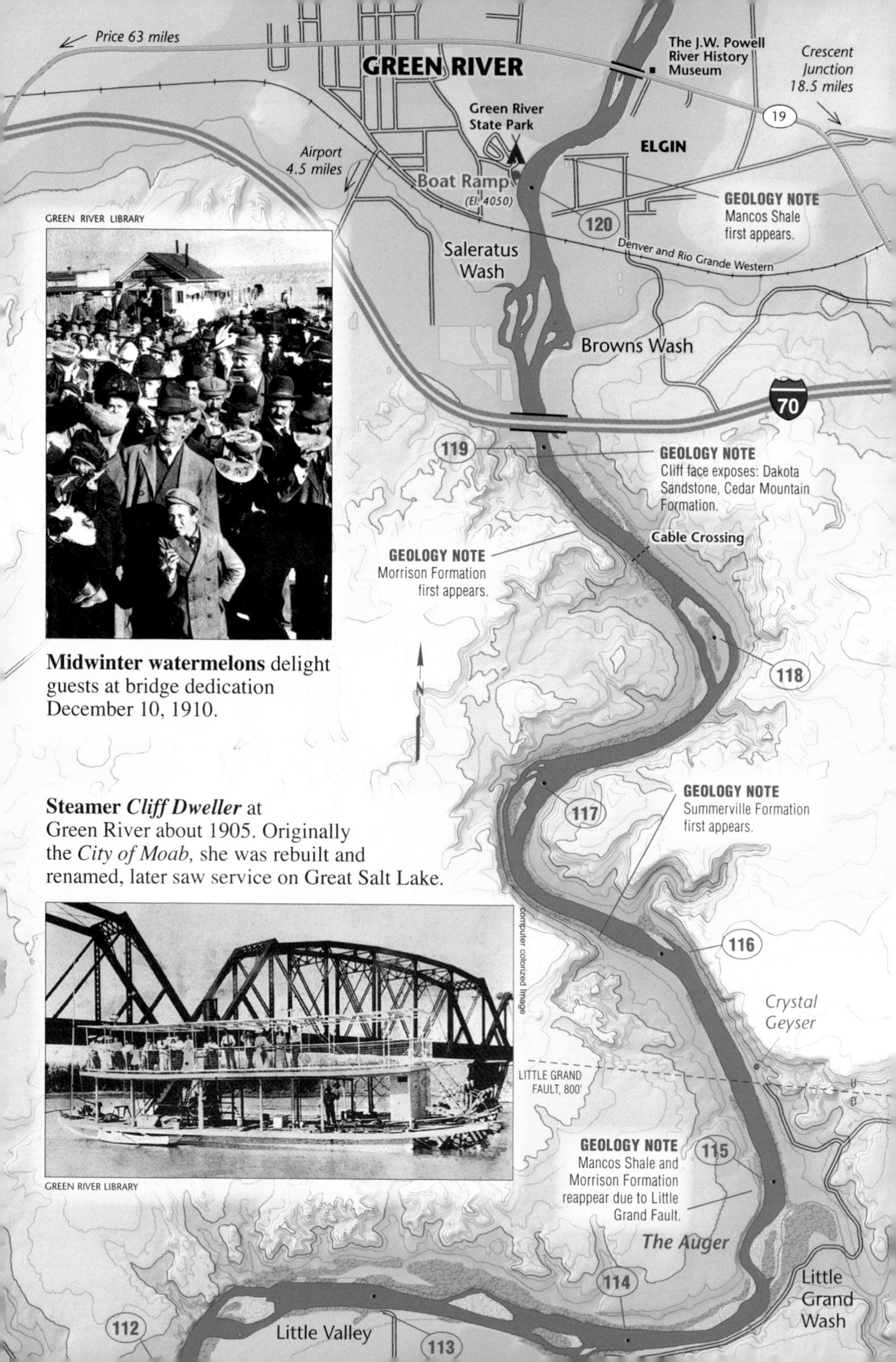

GREEN RIVER LIBRARY

Midwinter watermelons delight guests at bridge dedication December 10, 1910.

Steamer *Cliff Dweller* at Green River about 1905. Originally the *City of Moab,* she was rebuilt and renamed, later saw service on Great Salt Lake.

computer colorized image

GREEN RIVER LIBRARY

to examine some interesting rocks, deposited by mineral springs that at one time must have existed here, but are no longer flowing."

J.W. Powell

Powell Report

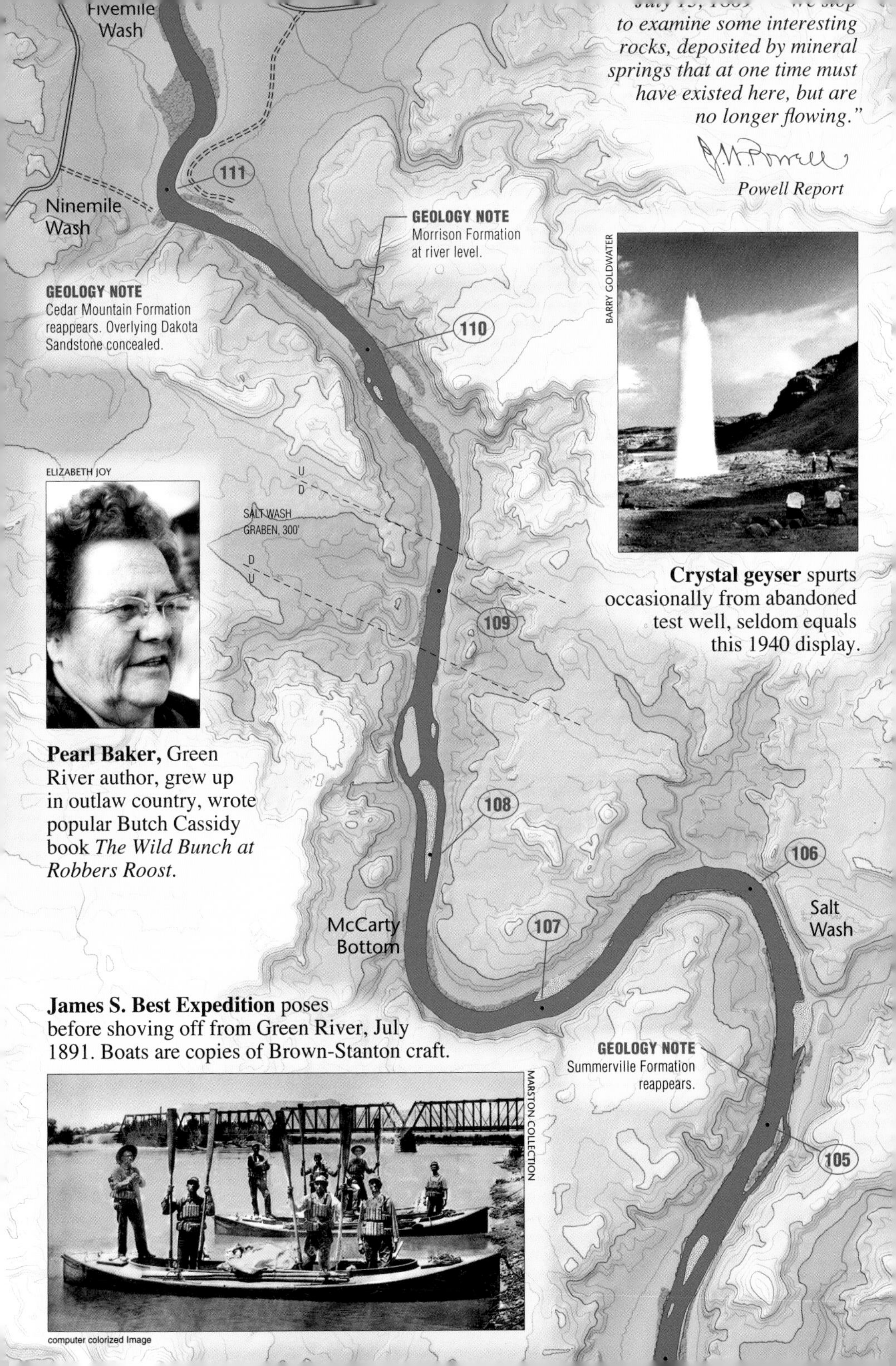

BARRY GOLDWATER

Crystal geyser spurts occasionally from abandoned test well, seldom equals this 1940 display.

ELIZABETH JOY

Pearl Baker, Green River author, grew up in outlaw country, wrote popular Butch Cassidy book *The Wild Bunch at Robbers Roost*.

James S. Best Expedition poses before shoving off from Green River, July 1891. Boats are copies of Brown-Stanton craft.

MARSTON COLLECTION

computer colorized Image

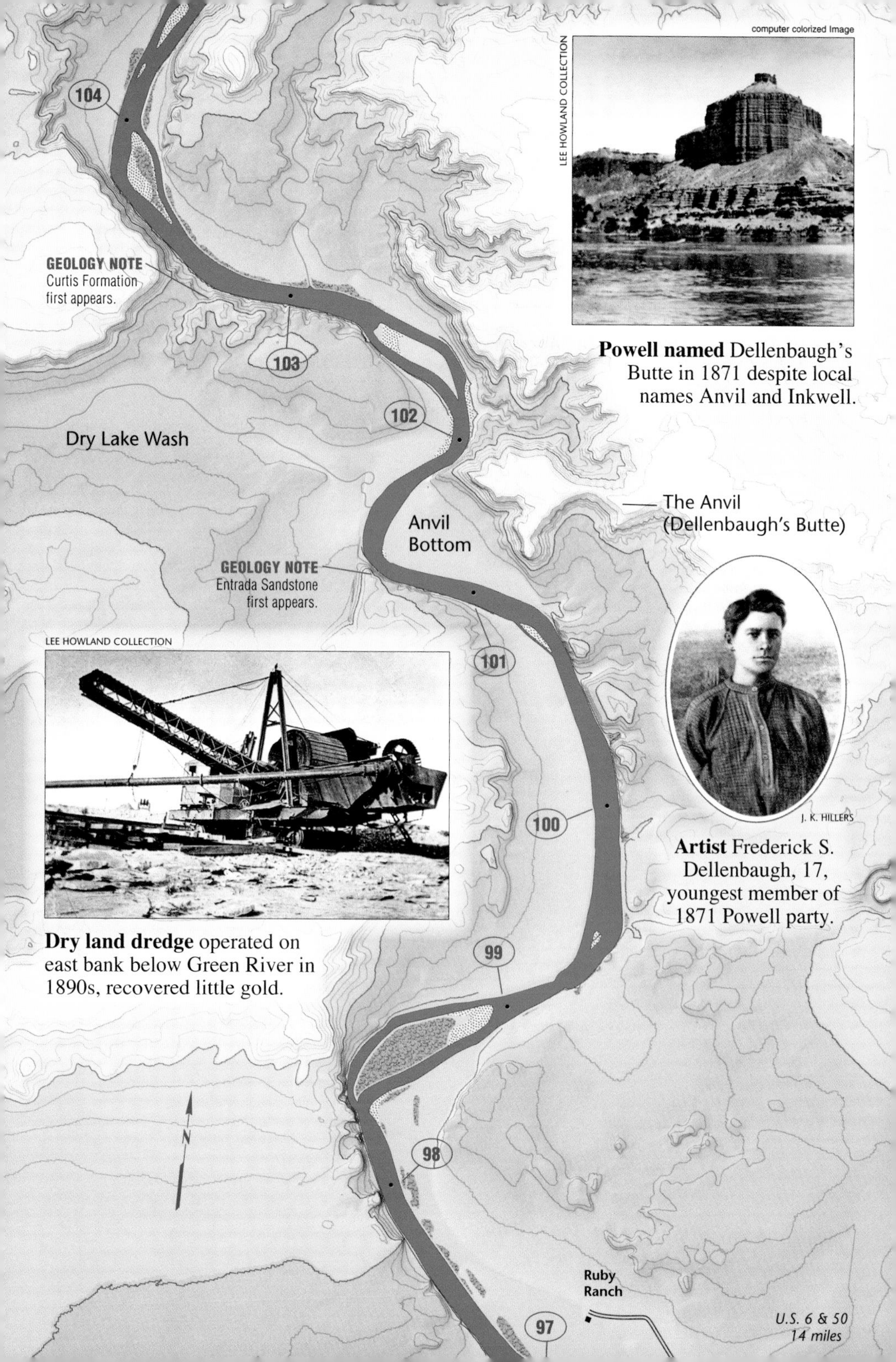

computer colorized Image

LEE HOWLAND COLLECTION

Powell named Dellenbaugh's Butte in 1871 despite local names Anvil and Inkwell.

J. K. HILLERS

Artist Frederick S. Dellenbaugh, 17, youngest member of 1871 Powell party.

LEE HOWLAND COLLECTION

Dry land dredge operated on east bank below Green River in 1890s, recovered little gold.

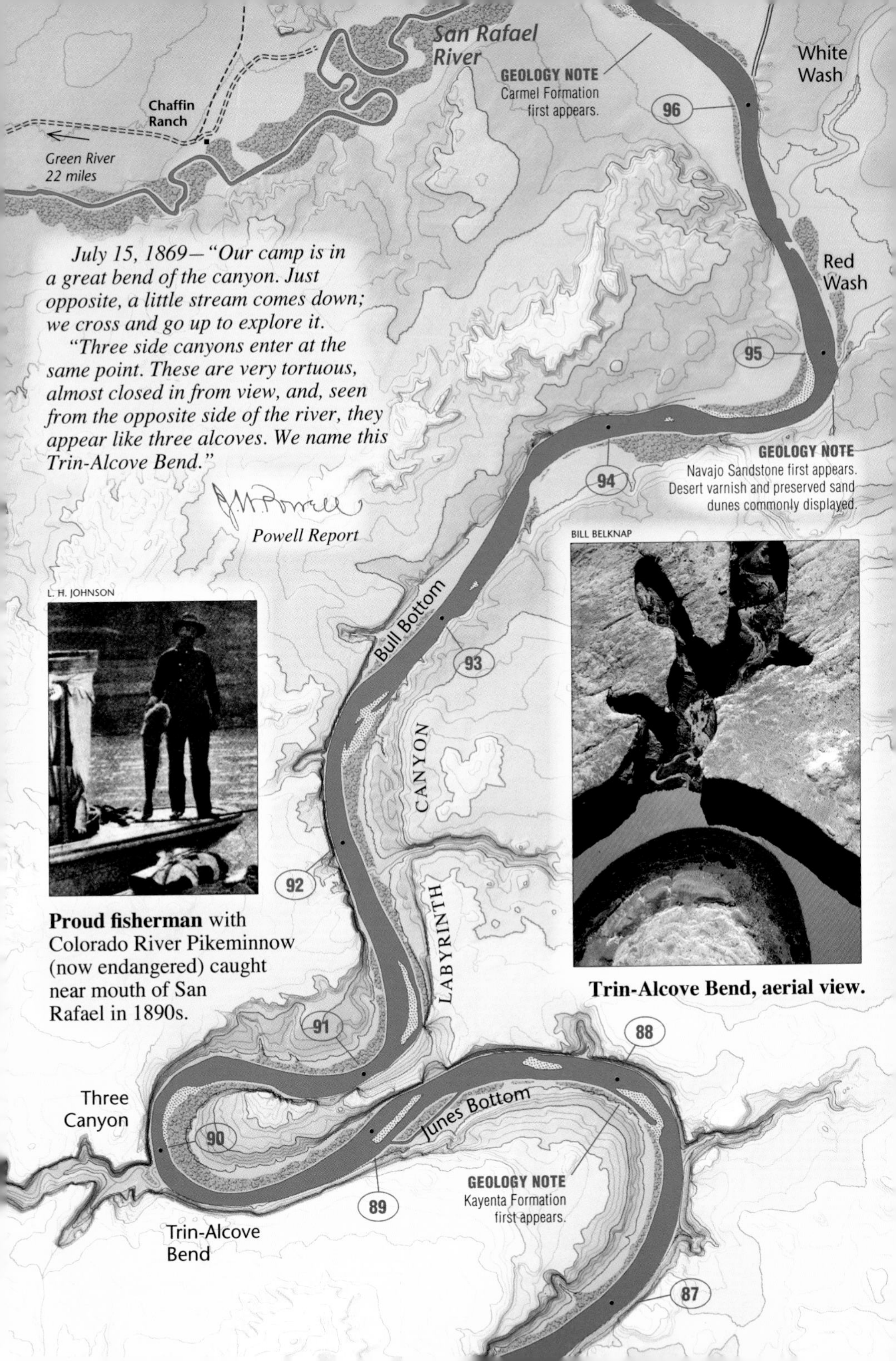

July 15, 1869—"Our camp is in a great bend of the canyon. Just opposite, a little stream comes down; we cross and go up to explore it.

"Three side canyons enter at the same point. These are very tortuous, almost closed in from view, and, seen from the opposite side of the river, they appear like three alcoves. We name this Trin-Alcove Bend."

J.W. Powell

Powell Report

L. H. JOHNSON

Proud fisherman with Colorado River Pikeminnow (now endangered) caught near mouth of San Rafael in 1890s.

BILL BELKNAP

Trin-Alcove Bend, aerial view.

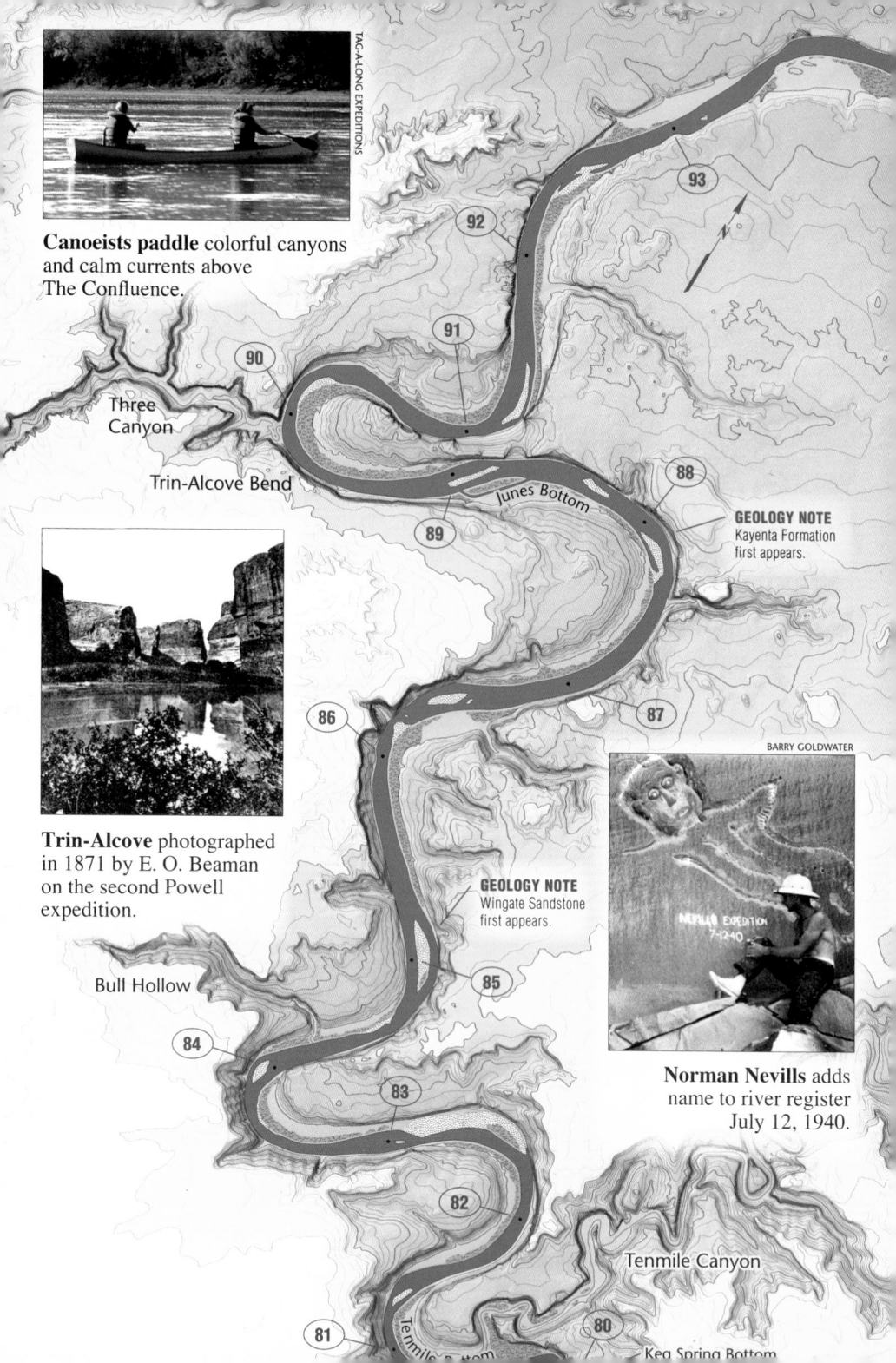

Canoeists paddle colorful canyons and calm currents above The Confluence.

Trin-Alcove photographed in 1871 by E. O. Beaman on the second Powell expedition.

Norman Nevills adds name to river register July 12, 1940.

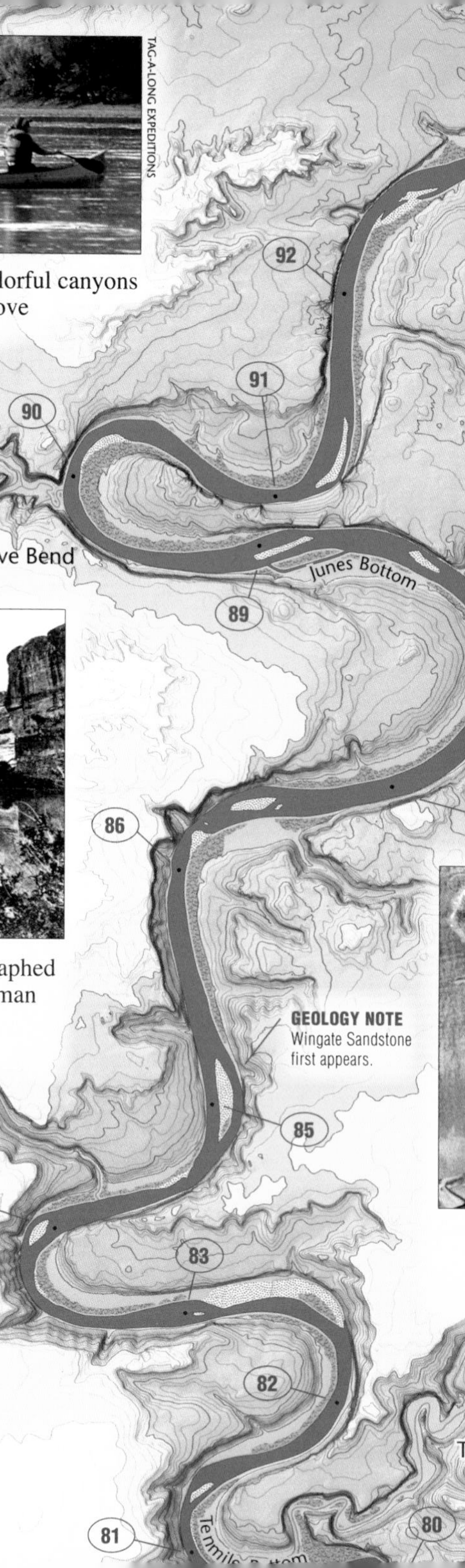

July 13, 1869 — We go around a great bend to the right, five miles, and come back to within a quarter of a mile of where we started. Then we sweep another great bend to the left, nine miles, and come back to within 600 yards of the beginning of the bend. The men call it a 'bowknot' of river; so we name it Bowknot Bend."

J.W. Powell

Powell Report

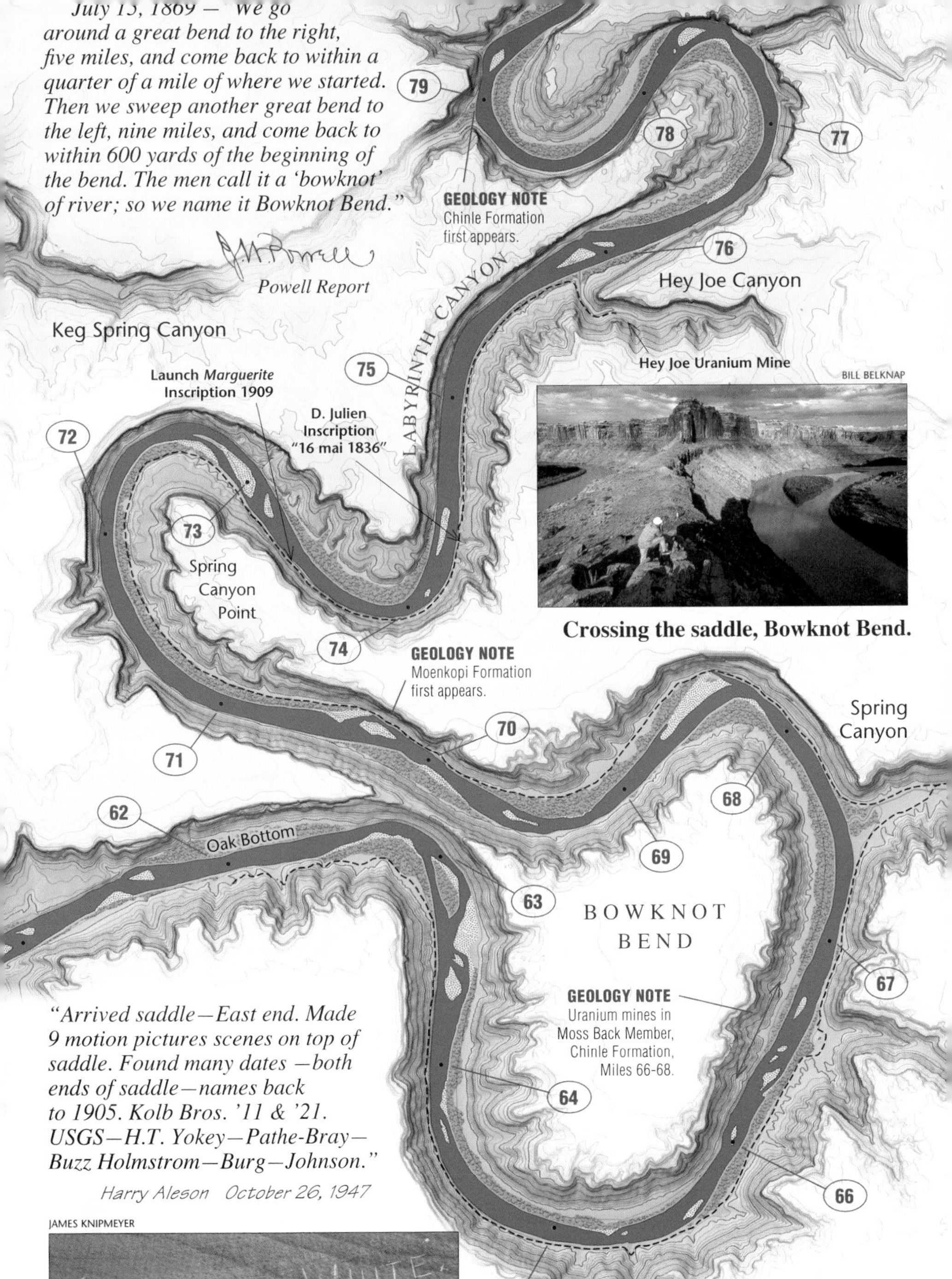

BILL BELKNAP

Crossing the saddle, Bowknot Bend.

"Arrived saddle—East end. Made 9 motion pictures scenes on top of saddle. Found many dates —both ends of saddle—names back to 1905. Kolb Bros. '11 & '21. USGS—H.T. Yokey—Pathe-Bray—Buzz Holmstrom—Burg—Johnson."

Harry Aleson October 26, 1947

JAMES KNIPMEYER

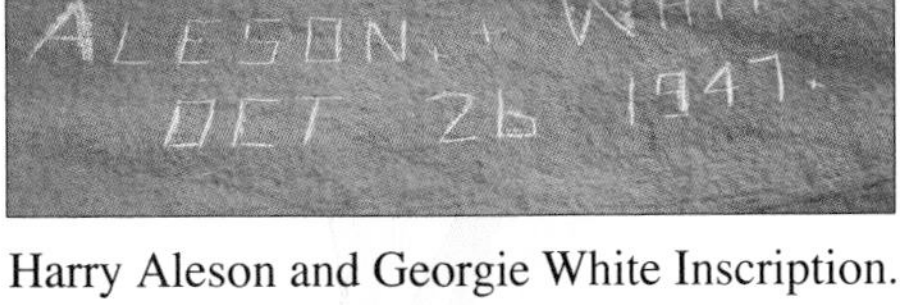

Harry Aleson and Georgie White Inscription.

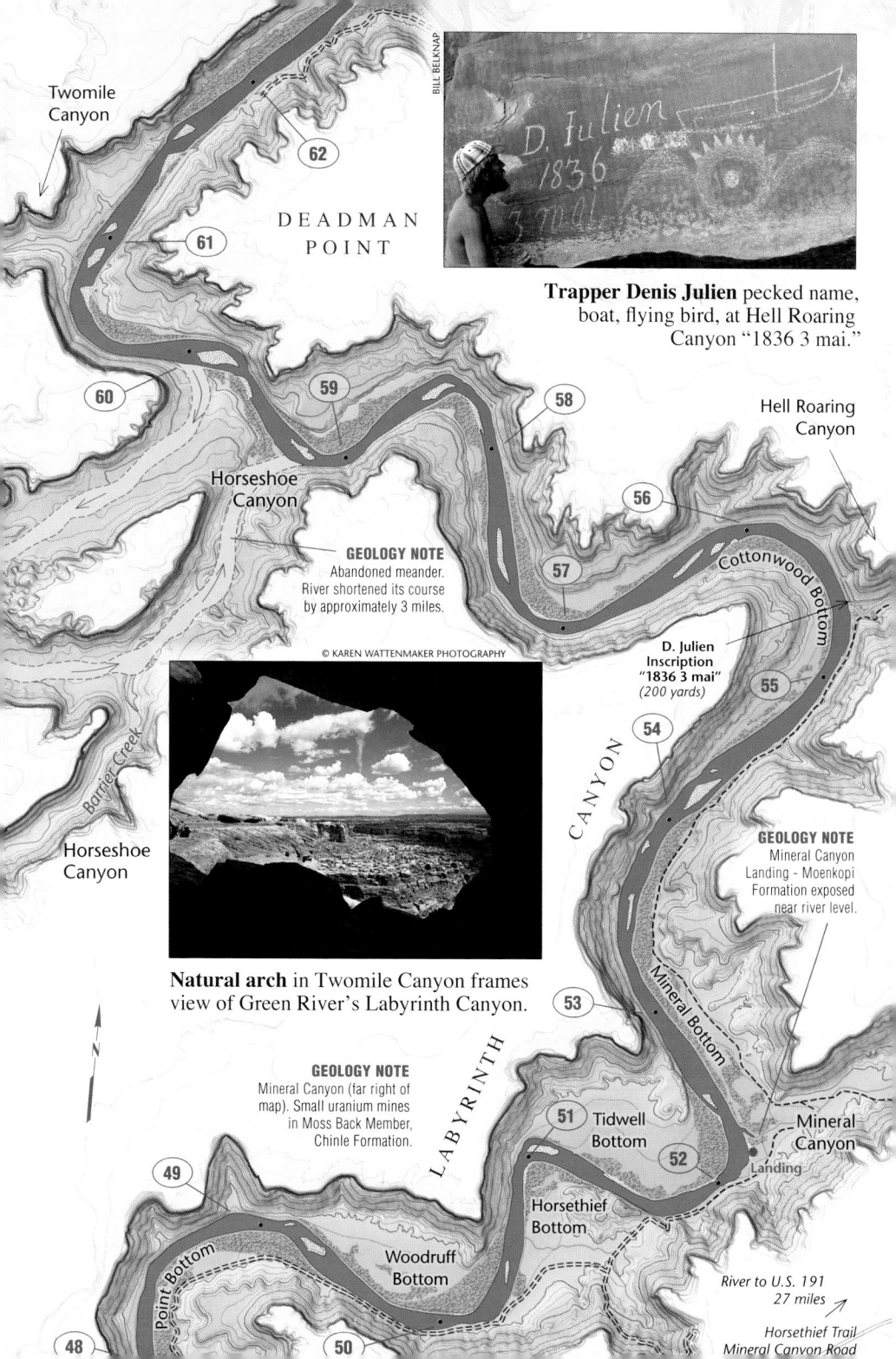

Trapper Denis Julien pecked name, boat, flying bird, at Hell Roaring Canyon "1836 3 mai."

Natural arch in Twomile Canyon frames view of Green River's Labyrinth Canyon.

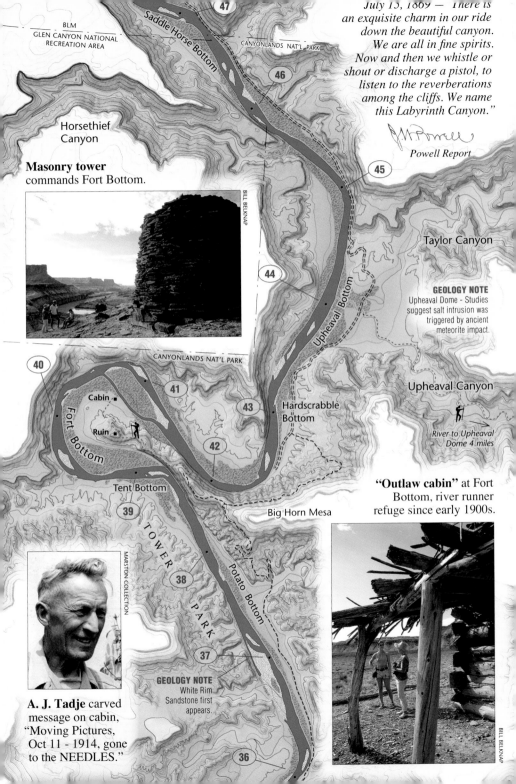

July 13, 1869 — "There is an exquisite charm in our ride down the beautiful canyon. We are all in fine spirits. Now and then we whistle or shout or discharge a pistol, to listen to the reverberations among the cliffs. We name this Labyrinth Canyon."

J.W. Powell

Powell Report

GEOLOGY NOTE
Upheaval Dome - Studies suggest salt intrusion was triggered by ancient meteorite impact.

Masonry tower commands Fort Bottom.

BILL BELKNAP

"Outlaw cabin" at Fort Bottom, river runner refuge since early 1900s.

BILL BELKNAP

GEOLOGY NOTE
White Rim Sandstone first appears.

MARSTON COLLECTION

A. J. Tadje carved message on cabin, "Moving Pictures, Oct 11 - 1914, gone to the NEEDLES."

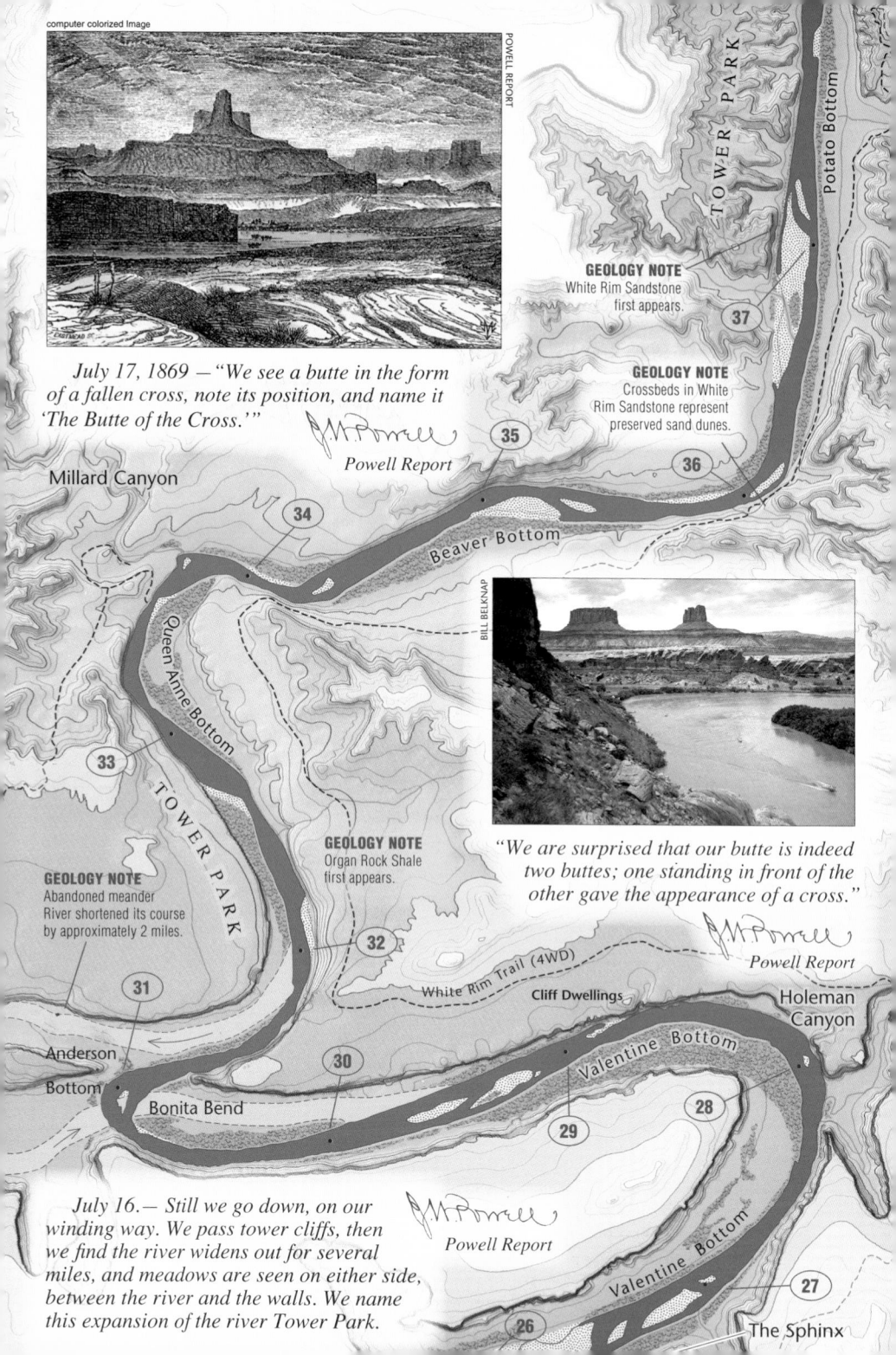

computer colorized Image

POWELL REPORT

July 17, 1869 — "We see a butte in the form of a fallen cross, note its position, and name it 'The Butte of the Cross.'"

J.W. Powell
Powell Report

BILL BELKNAP

"We are surprised that our butte is indeed two buttes; one standing in front of the other gave the appearance of a cross."

J.W. Powell
Powell Report

July 16.— Still we go down, on our winding way. We pass tower cliffs, then we find the river widens out for several miles, and meadows are seen on either side, between the river and the walls. We name this expansion of the river Tower Park.

J.W. Powell
Powell Report

TOWER PARK
Potato Bottom
GEOLOGY NOTE
White Rim Sandstone first appears.
37
GEOLOGY NOTE
Crossbeds in White Rim Sandstone represent preserved sand dunes.
35
36
Millard Canyon
34
Beaver Bottom
Queen Anne Bottom
33
TOWER PARK
GEOLOGY NOTE
Organ Rock Shale first appears.
GEOLOGY NOTE
Abandoned meander
River shortened its course by approximately 2 miles.
32
White Rim Trail (4WD)
31
Cliff Dwellings
Holeman Canyon
Anderson Bottom
Bonita Bend
30
Valentine Bottom
29
28
Valentine Bottom
27
26
The Sphinx

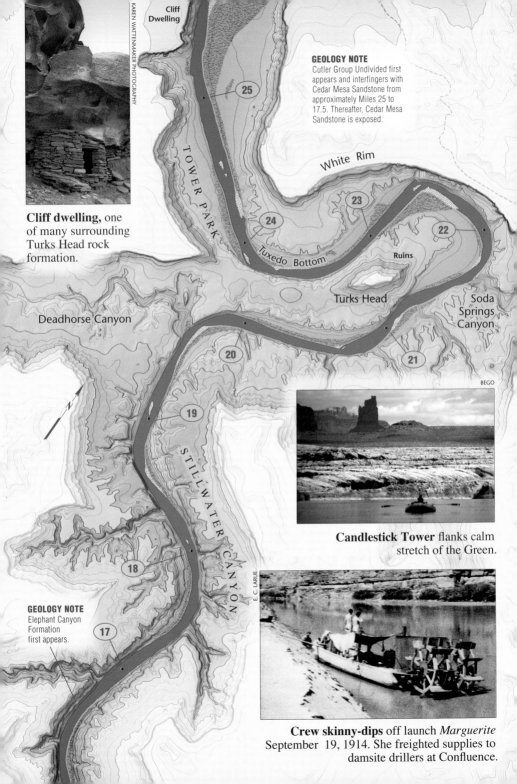

KAREN WATTENMAKER PHOTOGRAPHY

Cliff dwelling, one of many surrounding Turks Head rock formation.

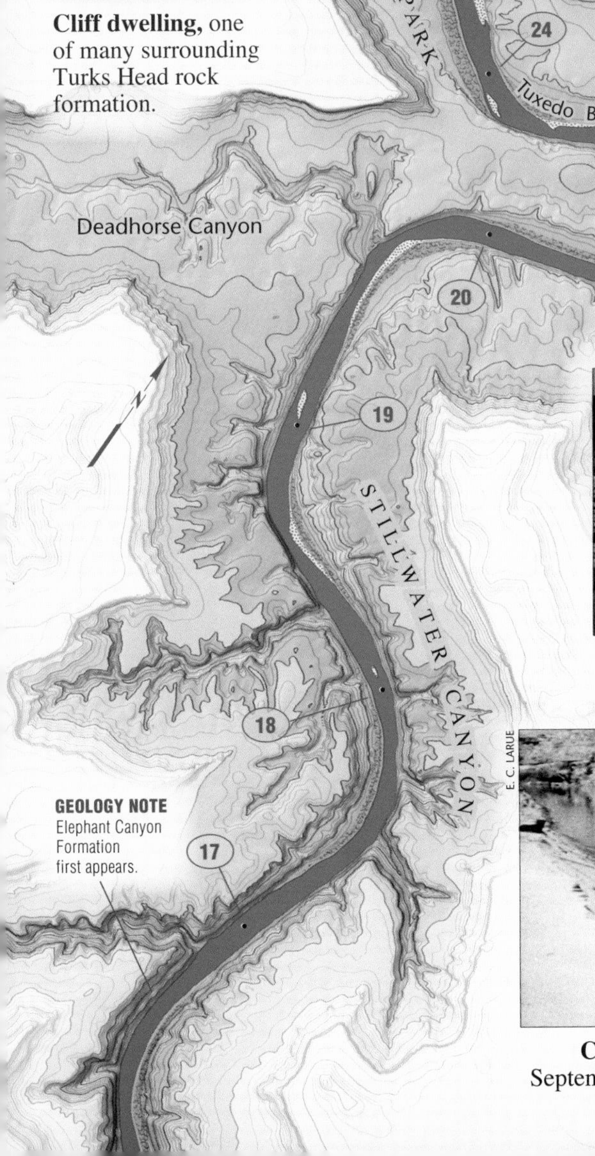

GEOLOGY NOTE
Cutler Group Undivided first appears and interfingers with Cedar Mesa Sandstone from approximately Miles 25 to 17.5. Thereafter, Cedar Mesa Sandstone is exposed.

GEOLOGY NOTE
Elephant Canyon Formation first appears.

BEGO

Candlestick Tower flanks calm stretch of the Green.

E. C. LARUE

Crew skinny-dips off launch *Marguerite* September 19, 1914. She freighted supplies to damsite drillers at Confluence.

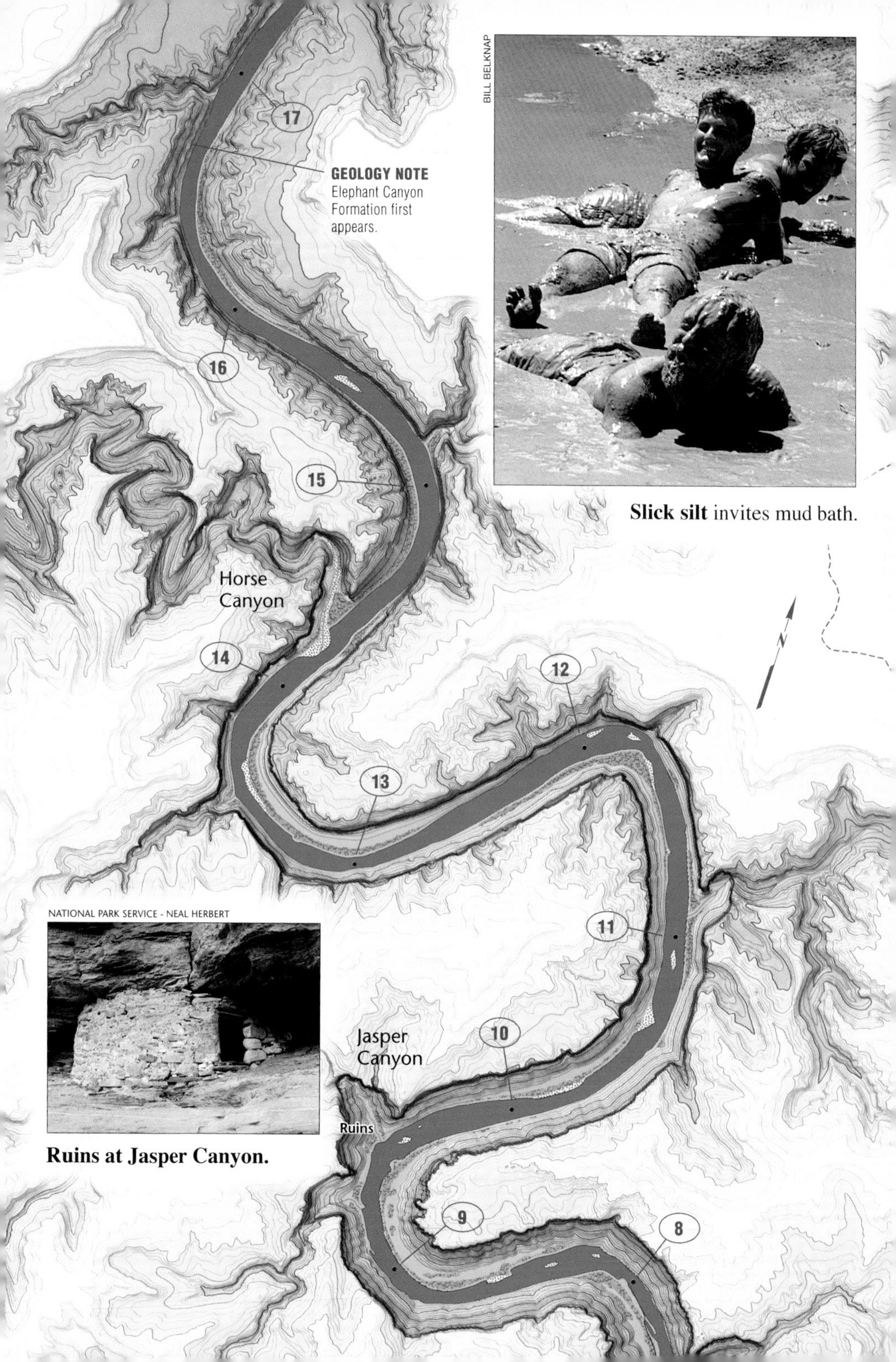

BILL BELKNAP

Slick silt invites mud bath.

NATIONAL PARK SERVICE - NEAL HERBERT

Ruins at Jasper Canyon.

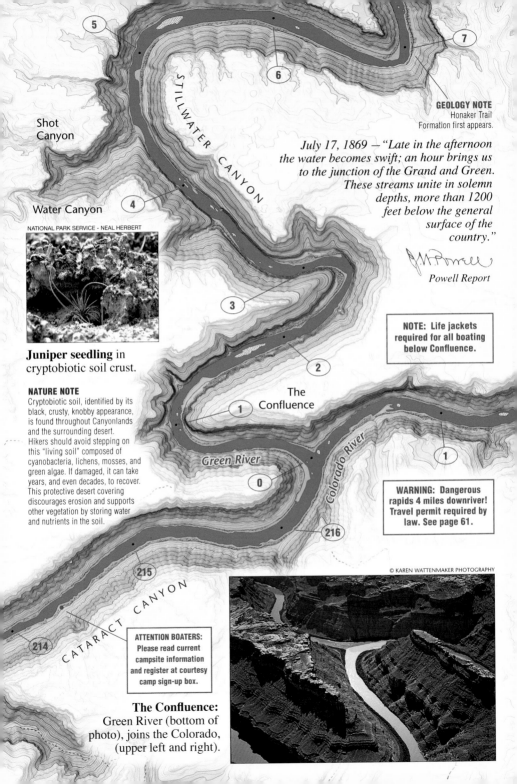

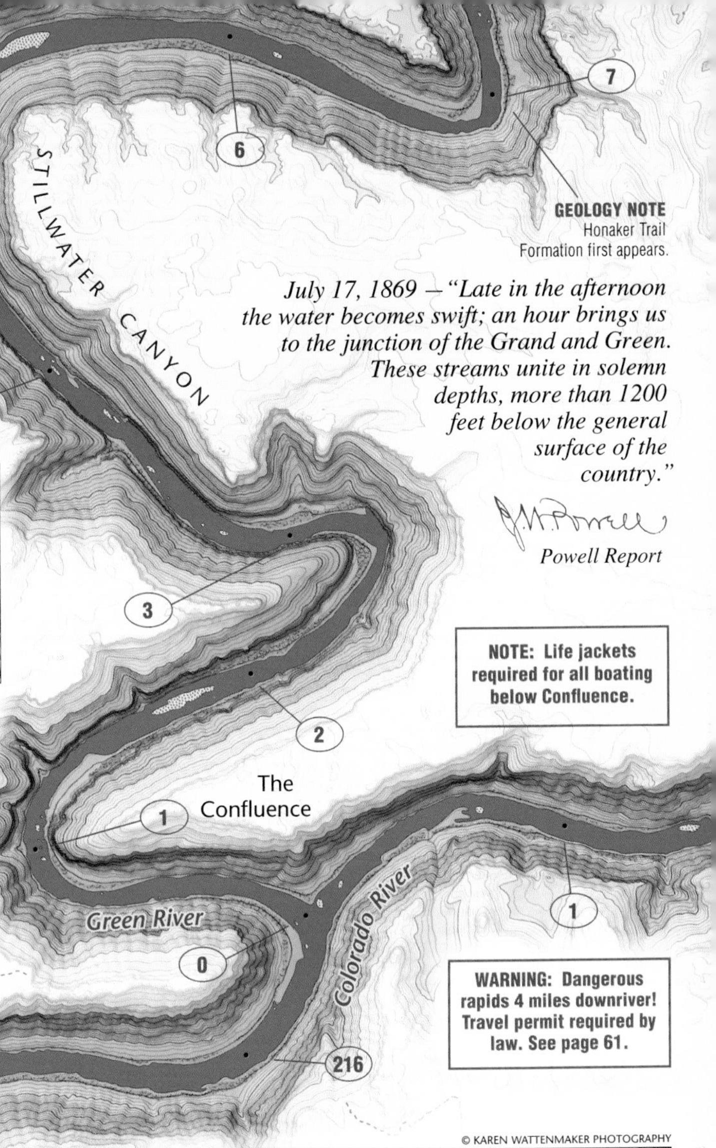

GEOLOGY NOTE
Honaker Trail Formation first appears.

July 17, 1869 — "Late in the afternoon the water becomes swift; an hour brings us to the junction of the Grand and Green. These streams unite in solemn depths, more than 1200 feet below the general surface of the country."

J. W. Powell

Powell Report

NATIONAL PARK SERVICE - NEAL HERBERT

Juniper seedling in cryptobiotic soil crust.

NATURE NOTE
Cryptobiotic soil, identified by its black, crusty, knobby appearance, is found throughout Canyonlands and the surrounding desert. Hikers should avoid stepping on this "living soil" composed of cyanobacteria, lichens, mosses, and green algae. If damaged, it can take years, and even decades, to recover. This protective desert covering discourages erosion and supports other vegetation by storing water and nutrients in the soil.

NOTE: Life jackets required for all boating below Confluence.

WARNING: Dangerous rapids 4 miles downriver! Travel permit required by law. **See page 61.**

ATTENTION BOATERS: Please read current campsite information and register at courtesy camp sign-up box.

The Confluence: Green River (bottom of photo), joins the Colorado, (upper left and right).

HORSETHIEF/RUBY

After a tumultuous descent from its mountainous upper reaches, the Colorado River makes a relatively tranquil entry into Canyonlands country. Horsethief and Ruby canyons are noted for magnificent scenery, interesting history, and splendid side canyon hikes. Often traversed in a single day or with an overnight at one of several excellent campsites, this 25-mile stretch is commonly boated in open canoes, kayaks, and small rafts.

Located within McInnis Canyons National Conservation Area, much of the land on the south side of the river also lies within Black Ridge Canyons Wilderness Area; both are managed by the Bureau of Land Management. Boaters should be aware of pockets of private land on both sides of the river and respect the rights of landowners.

No permit is currently required for private trips, although the BLM requests that, as a courtesy, boaters register and sign up for campsites at the Loma boat ramp. For up-to-date boating requirements on safety, sanitation, and camping contact: Bureau of Land Management, Grand Junction Resource Area, 1815 H. Road, Grand Junction, CO 81506 (970) 244-3000 or http://www.blm.gov/co/st/en/fo/mcnca/recreation/boating/coriver.html.

Above photo: Denver and Rio Grande in Ruby Canyon early 1890s BY WILLIAM HENRY JACKSON

RIVER FLOW INFORMATION
CALL: 801-539-1311 or go to www.cbrfc.noaa.gov/

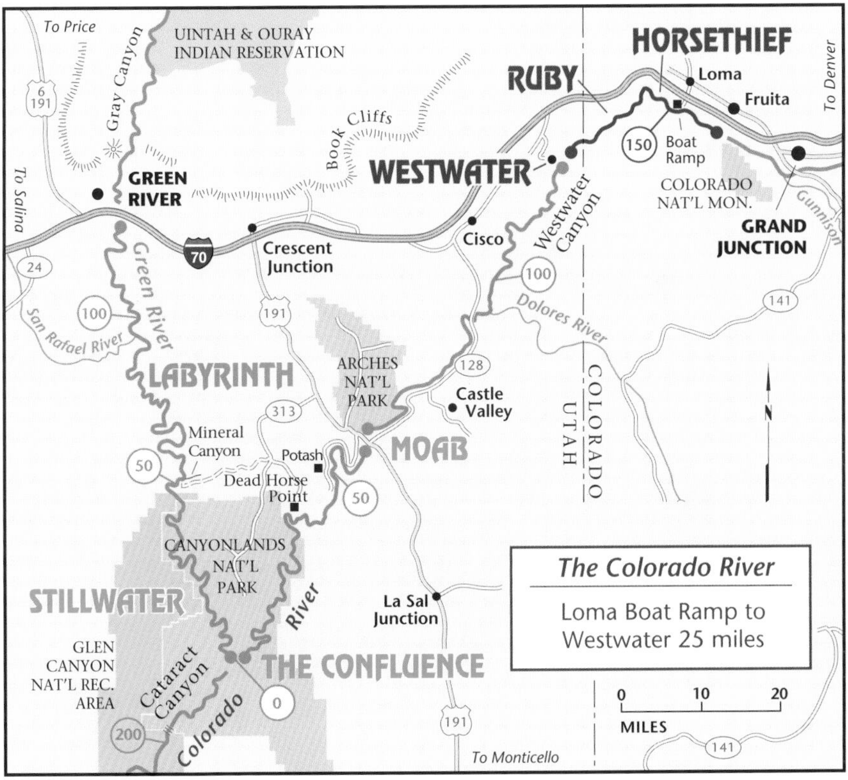

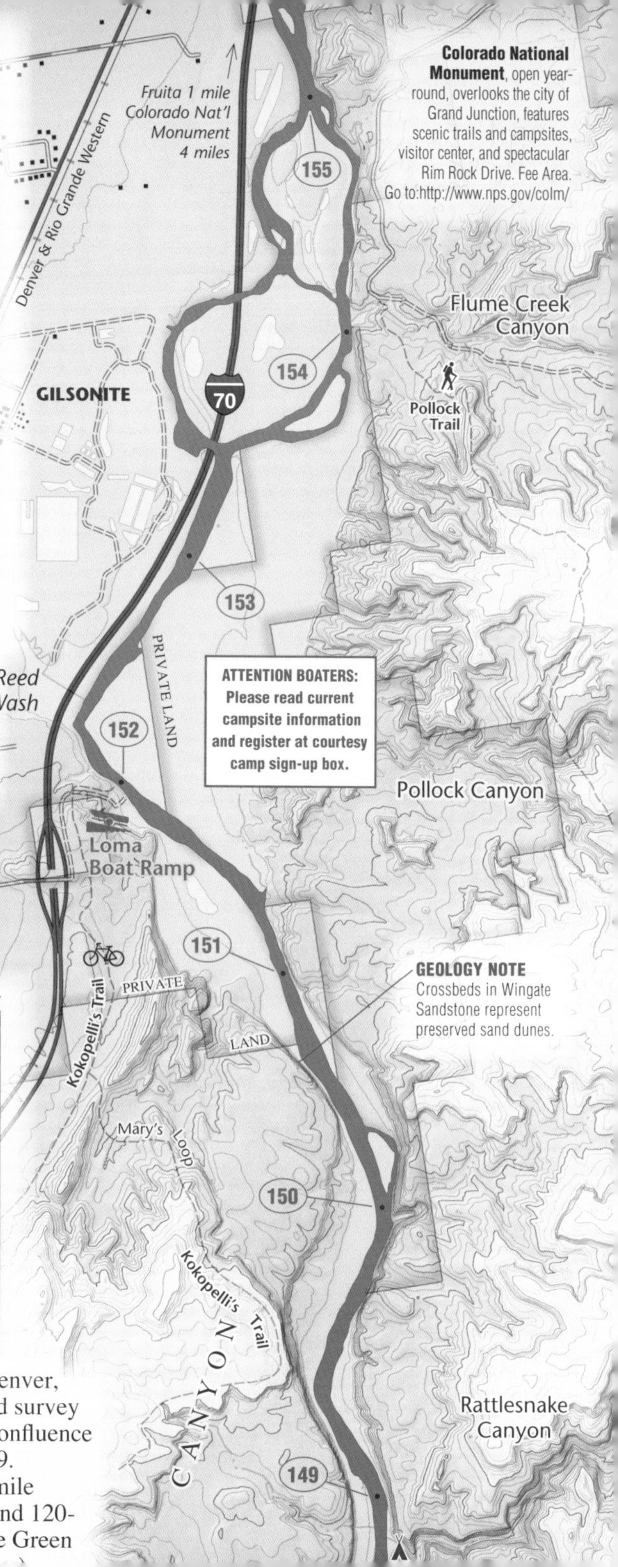

Colorado National Monument, open year-round, overlooks the city of Grand Junction, features scenic trails and campsites, visitor center, and spectacular Rim Rock Drive. Fee Area. Go to:http://www.nps.gov/colm/

ATTENTION BOATERS:
Please read current campsite information and register at courtesy camp sign-up box.

GEOLOGY NOTE
Crossbeds in Wingate Sandstone represent preserved sand dunes.

JOHN EVANS

Natural Arches in the Entrada Sandstone are accessible from the river via tough, steep trail up Rattlesnake Canyon or by 4-wheel drive road from Colorado National Monument.

COLORADO HISTORICAL SOCIETY

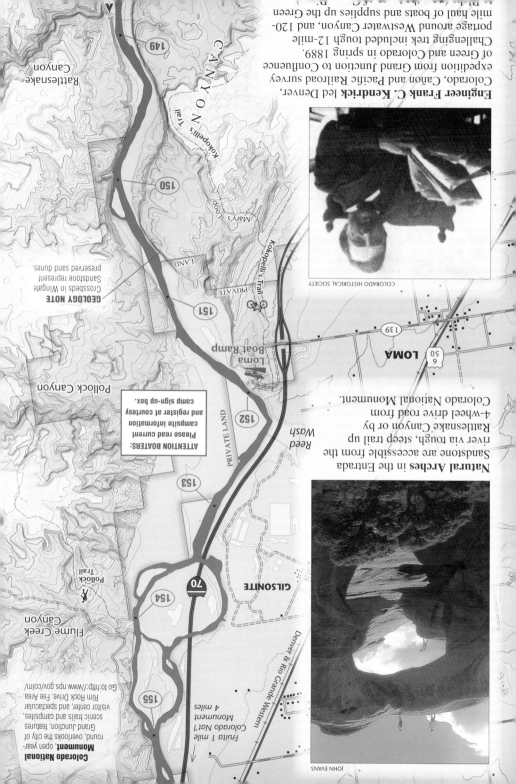

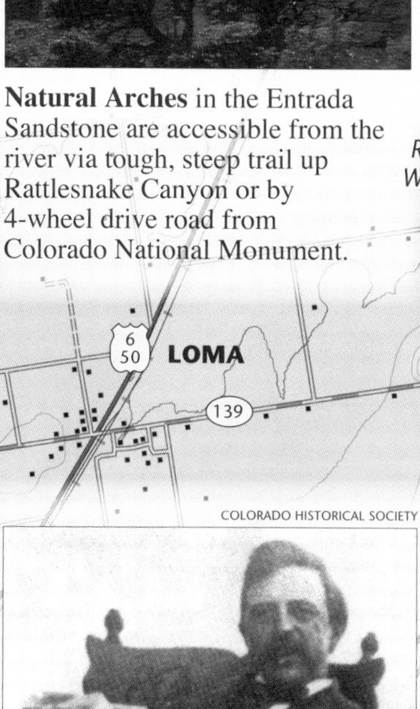

Engineer Frank C. Kendrick led Denver, Colorado, Cañon and Pacific Railroad survey expedition from Grand Junction to Confluence of Green and Colorado in spring 1889. Challenging trek included tough 12-mile portage around Westwater Canyon, and 120-mile haul of boats and supplies up the Green

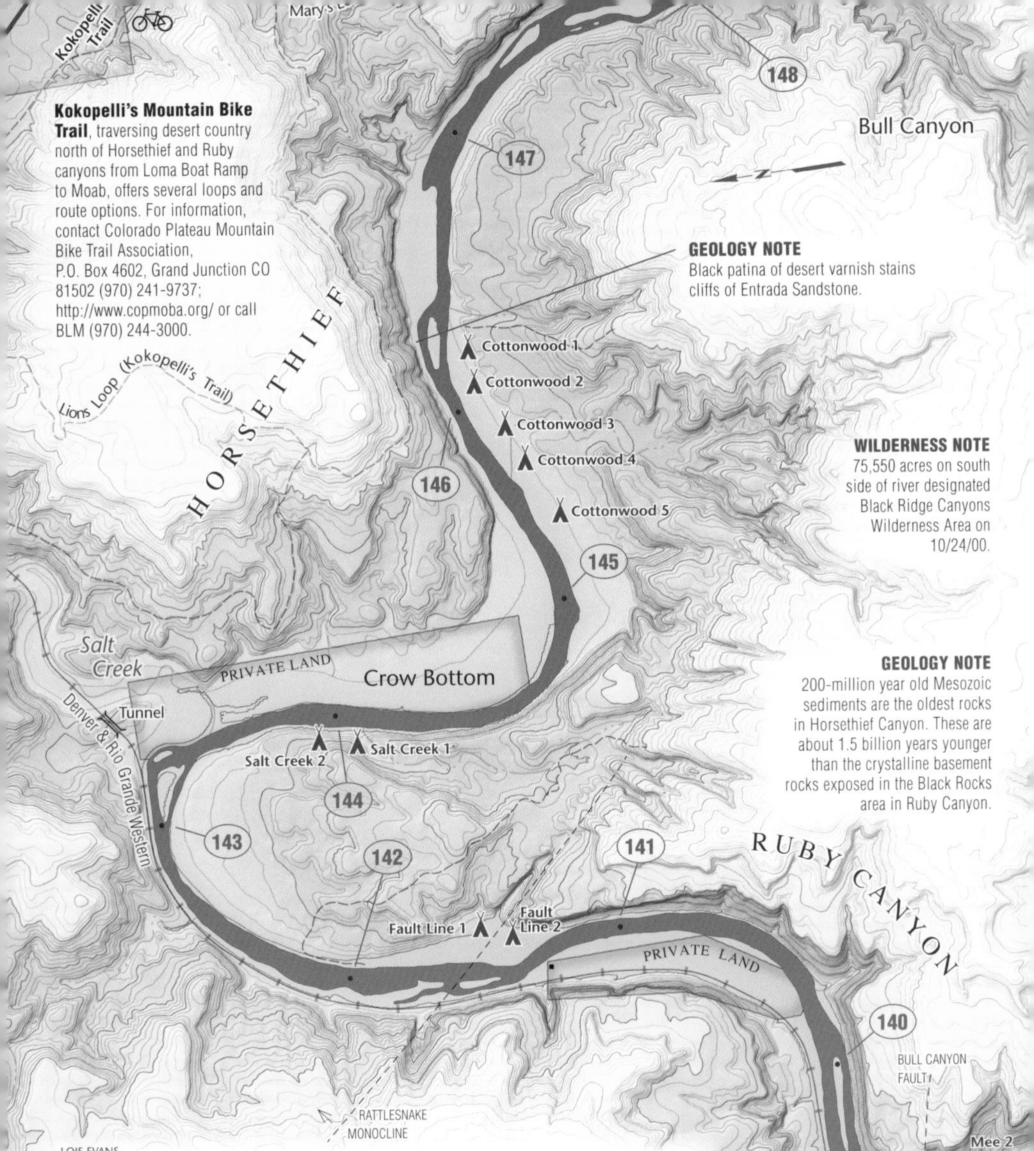
Mary's
Kokopelli Trail
Kokopelli's Mountain Bike Trail, traversing desert country north of Horsethief and Ruby canyons from Loma Boat Ramp to Moab, offers several loops and route options. For information, contact Colorado Plateau Mountain Bike Trail Association, P.O. Box 4602, Grand Junction CO 81502 (970) 241-9737; http://www.copmoba.org/ or call BLM (970) 244-3000.
148
147
Bull Canyon
GEOLOGY NOTE
Black patina of desert varnish stains cliffs of Entrada Sandstone.
HORSETHIEF
Lions Loop (Kokopelli's Trail)
Cottonwood 1
Cottonwood 2
Cottonwood 3
Cottonwood 4
Cottonwood 5
146
145
WILDERNESS NOTE
75,550 acres on south side of river designated Black Ridge Canyons Wilderness Area on 10/24/00.
Salt Creek
PRIVATE LAND
Crow Bottom
Tunnel
Denver & Rio Grande Western
Salt Creek 2
Salt Creek 1
144
143
142
141
GEOLOGY NOTE
200-million year old Mesozoic sediments are the oldest rocks in Horsethief Canyon. These are about 1.5 billion years younger than the crystalline basement rocks exposed in the Black Rocks area in Ruby Canyon.
RUBY CANYON
Fault Line 1
Fault Line 2
PRIVATE LAND
140
BULL CANYON FAULT
RATTLESNAKE MONOCLINE
Mee 2
Mee 1
Mee Corner
139
D U

LOIE EVANS

River cut reveals innards of dramatic **Rattlesnake Monocline** at Mile 141.5.

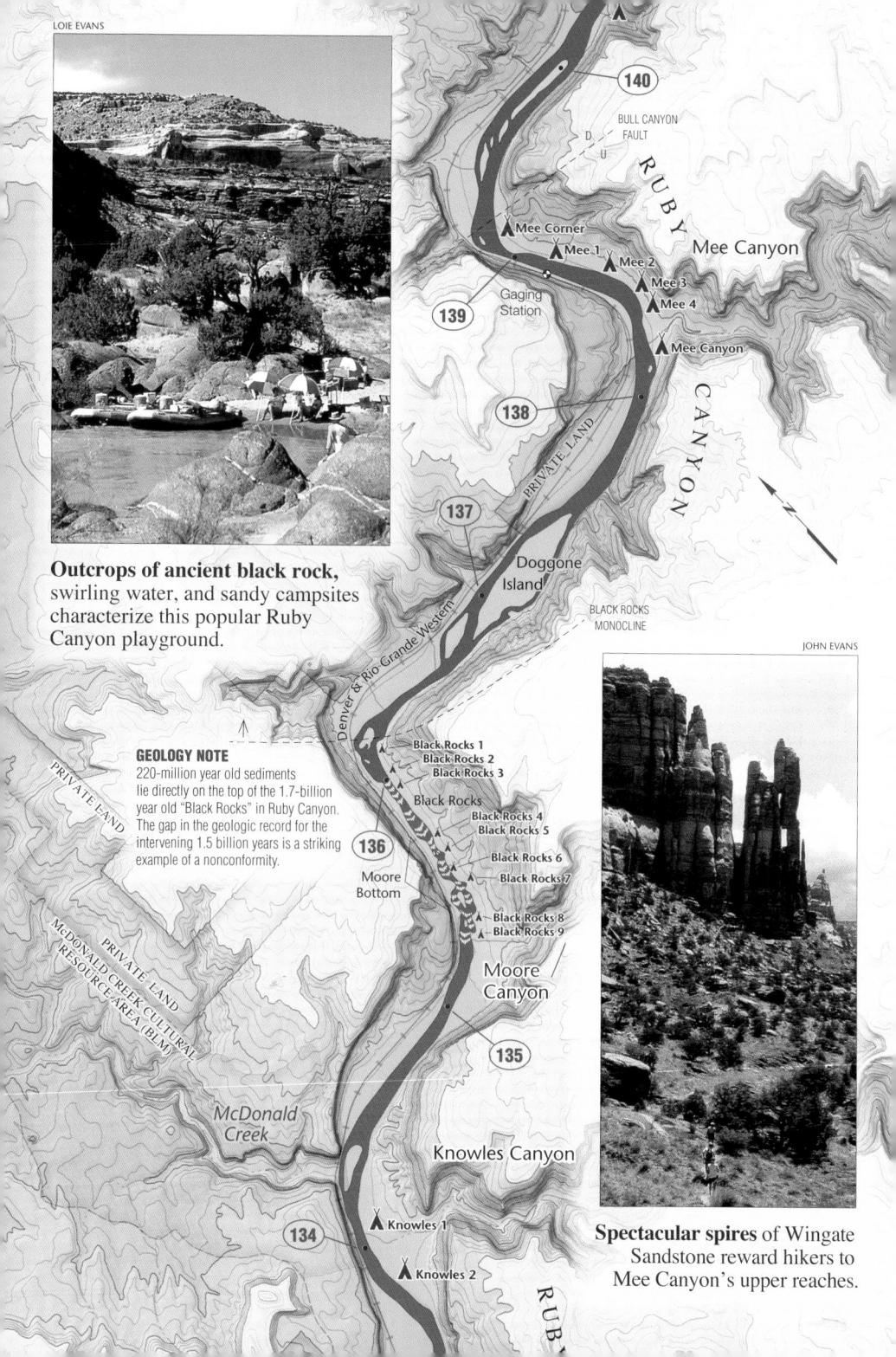

LOIE EVANS

Outcrops of ancient black rock, swirling water, and sandy campsites characterize this popular Ruby Canyon playground.

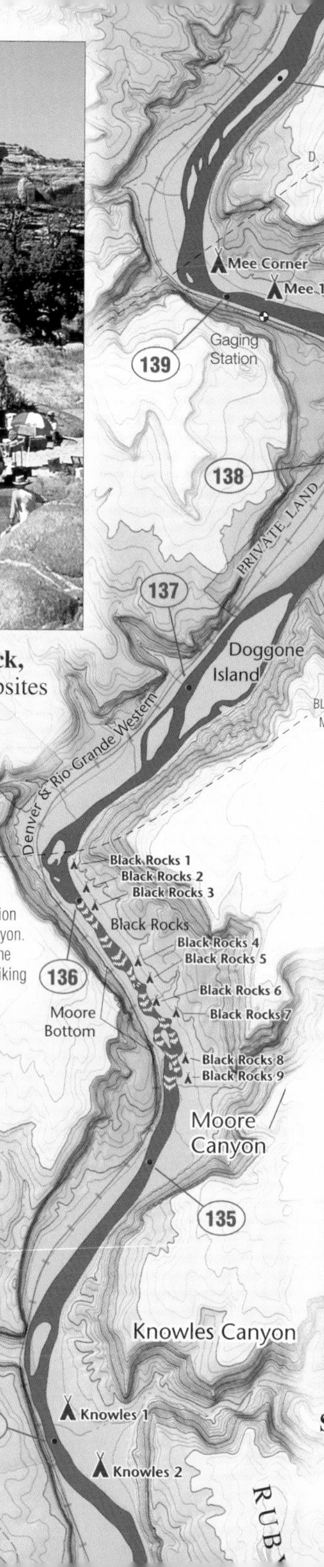

GEOLOGY NOTE

220-million year old sediments lie directly on the top of the 1.7-billion year old "Black Rocks" in Ruby Canyon. The gap in the geologic record for the intervening 1.5 billion years is a striking example of a nonconformity.

JOHN EVANS

Spectacular spires of Wingate Sandstone reward hikers to Mee Canyon's upper reaches.

Early river visitors painted rock art on McDonald Canyon walls a thousand years ago. Now protected by law, rare Fremont Culture treasures are part of the McDonald Creek Cultural Resource Management Area. Images may be viewed from a distance, but not touched.

LOIE EVANS

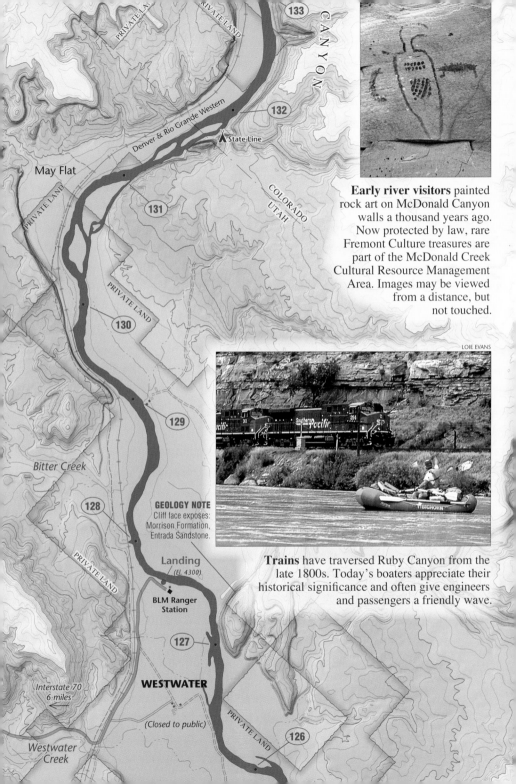

Trains have traversed Ruby Canyon from the late 1800s. Today's boaters appreciate their historical significance and often give engineers and passengers a friendly wave.

WESTWATER – MOAB

For a short whitewater run it's hard to beat Westwater's narrow rapids and unique black and red canyon. But it's no place for inexperienced boaters!

Known also as Hades or Granite Canyon, Westwater was seldom run until the early 1970s when more and more river enthusiasts began to appreciate it. Boating permits are required by the BLM year-round.

Below Westwater Canyon a long calm stretch winds past the Dolores River and Professor Valley. Then rocky riffles and rapids punctuate the Colorado beyond the Arches National Park boundary and to within a few miles of Moab. No permits are needed between the Dewey Bridge and the Potash Boat Ramp. The 13-mile stretch between Hittle Bottom and Takeout Beach is a popular daily river trip offering some splashes and spectacular scenery and can be run privately or with a commercial outfitter. The Bureau of Land Management administers this entire stretch of river and issues permits for Westwater Canyon. For information or a list of outfitters, contact BLM, 82 East Dogwood, Moab, UT 84532. (435)-259-2100 or http://www.ut.blm.gov/Recreation/recriverrunning.html.

Above photo: Boaters enjoy the thrill of Westwater Canyon's action-packed whitewater. WESTERN RIVER EXPEDITIONS

RIVER FLOW INFORMATION
CALL: 801-539-1311 or go to www.cbrfc.noaa.gov/

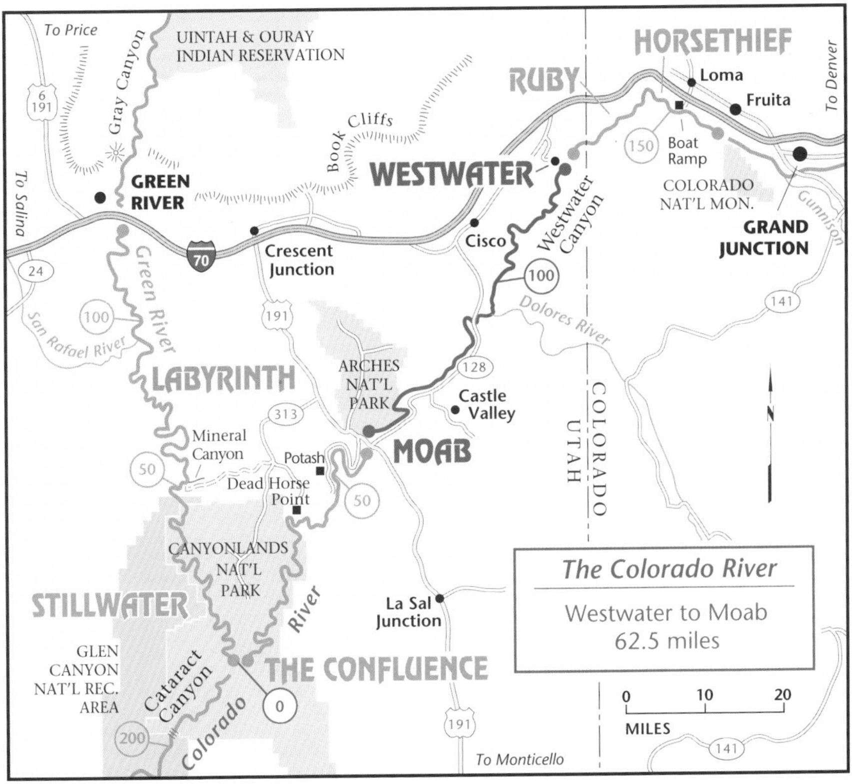

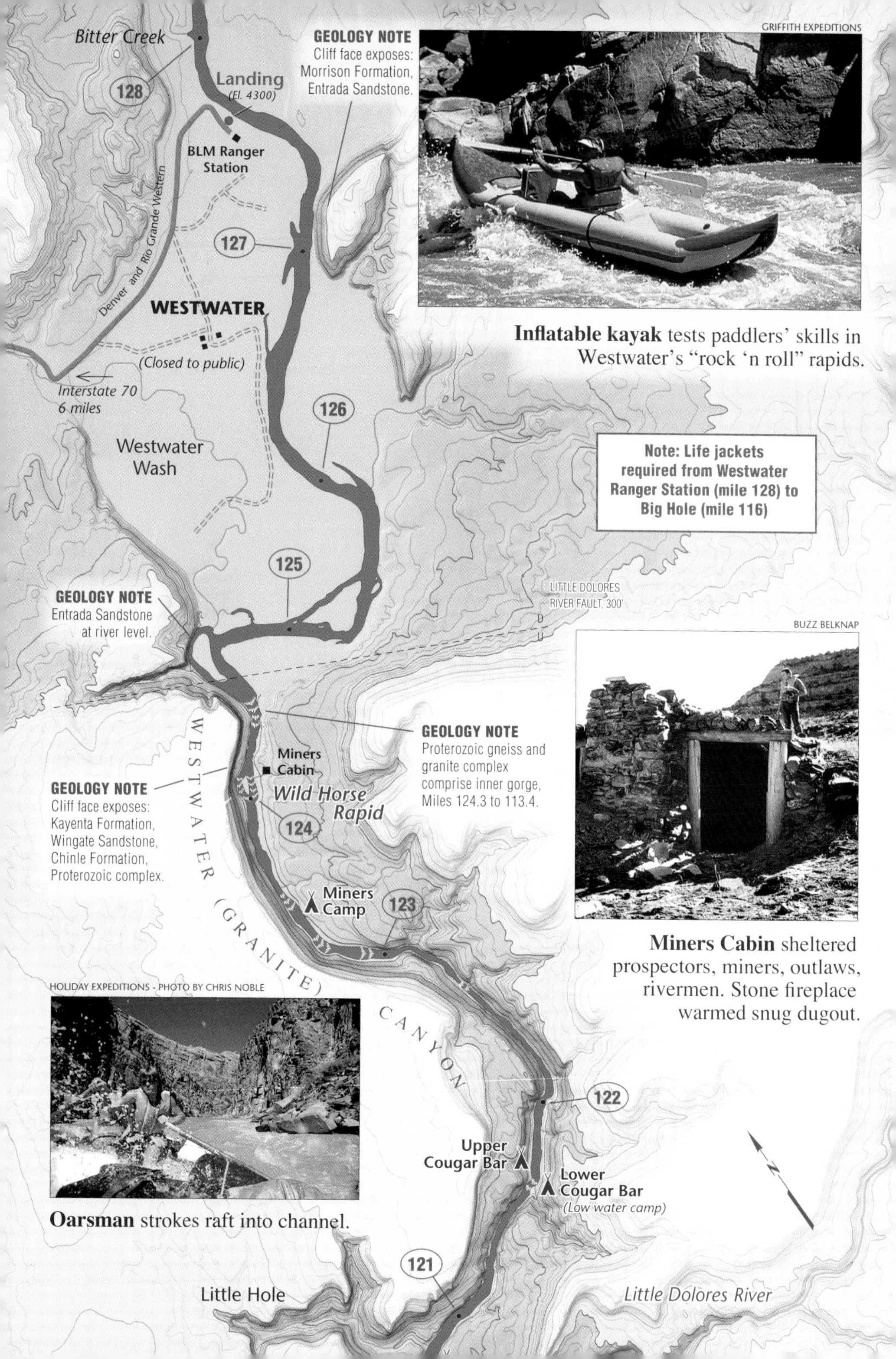

Note: Life jackets required from Westwater Ranger Station (mile 128) to Big Hole (mile 116)

GRIFFITH EXPEDITIONS

Inflatable kayak tests paddlers' skills in Westwater's "rock 'n roll" rapids.

BUZZ BELKNAP

Miners Cabin sheltered prospectors, miners, outlaws, rivermen. Stone fireplace warmed snug dugout.

HOLIDAY EXPEDITIONS - PHOTO BY CHRIS NOBLE

Oarsman strokes raft into channel.

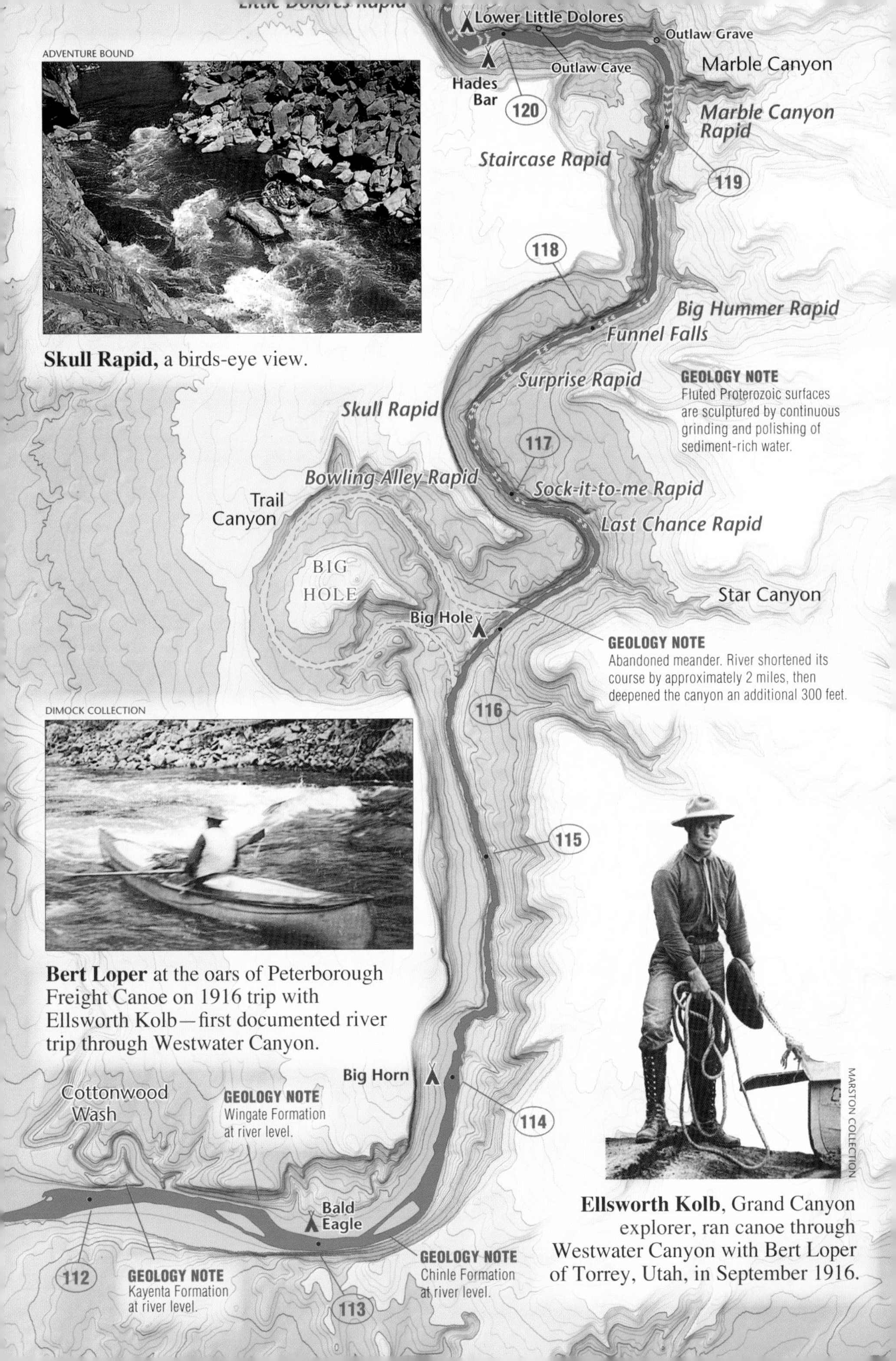

ADVENTURE BOUND

Skull Rapid, a birds-eye view.

DIMOCK COLLECTION

Bert Loper at the oars of Peterborough Freight Canoe on 1916 trip with Ellsworth Kolb—first documented river trip through Westwater Canyon.

MARSTON COLLECTION

Ellsworth Kolb, Grand Canyon explorer, ran canoe through Westwater Canyon with Bert Loper of Torrey, Utah, in September 1916.

GRIFFITH EXPEDITIONS

Golden Eagle launches into flight.

WESTERN RIVER EXPEDITIONS

Kids construct sand castle on river beach.

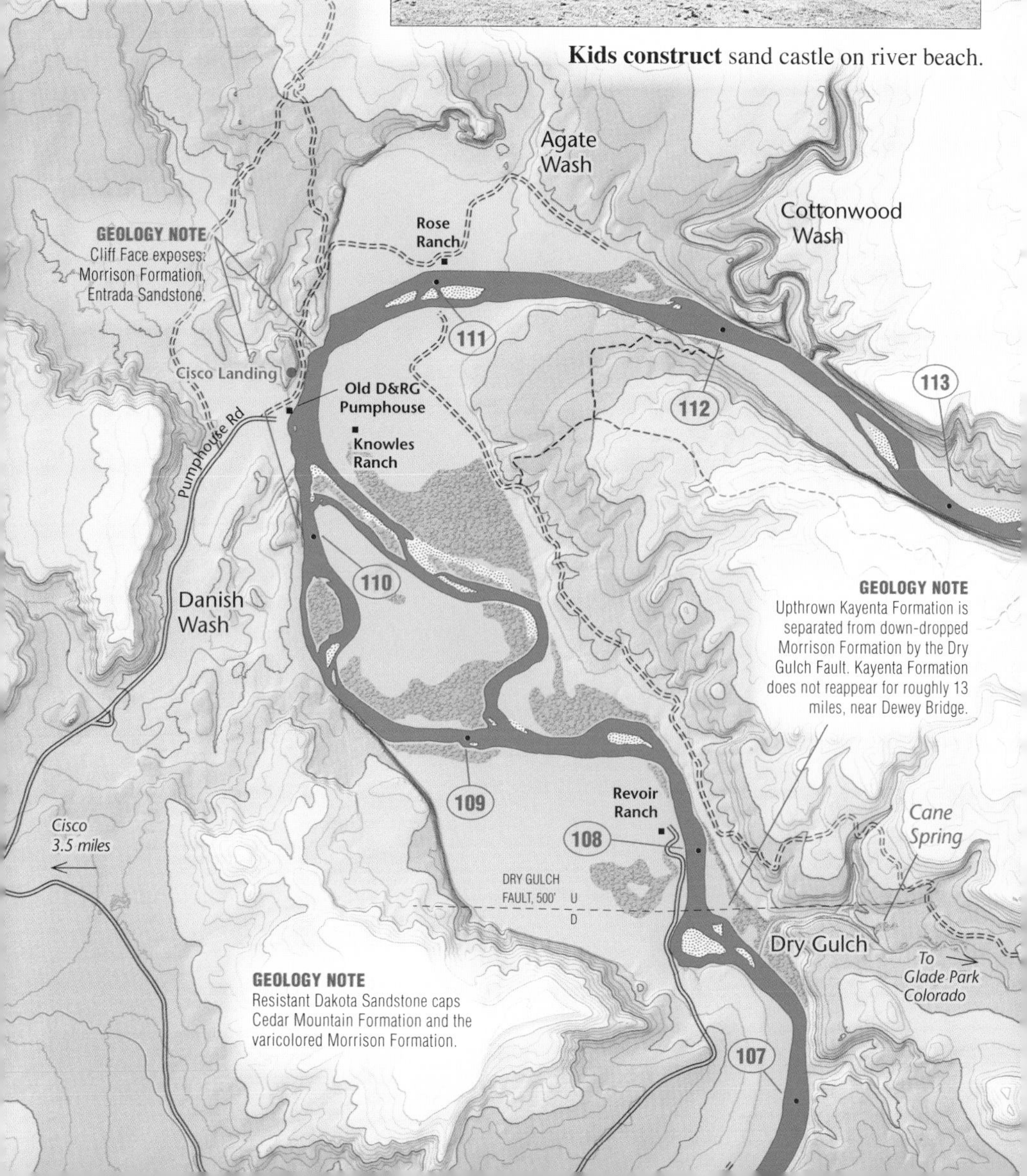

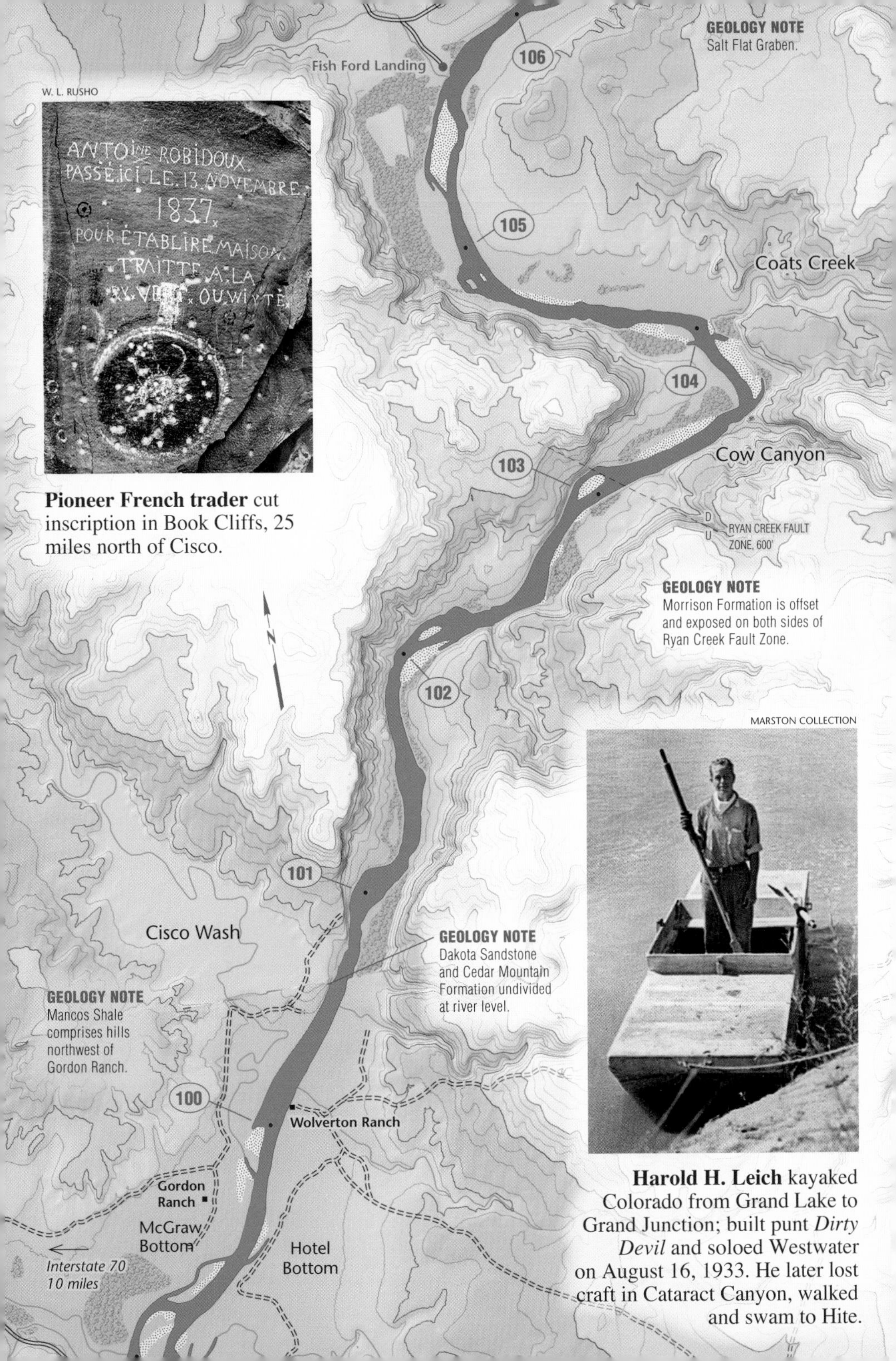

W. L. RUSHO

Pioneer French trader cut inscription in Book Cliffs, 25 miles north of Cisco.

MARSTON COLLECTION

Harold H. Leich kayaked Colorado from Grand Lake to Grand Junction; built punt *Dirty Devil* and soloed Westwater on August 16, 1933. He later lost craft in Cataract Canyon, walked and swam to Hite.

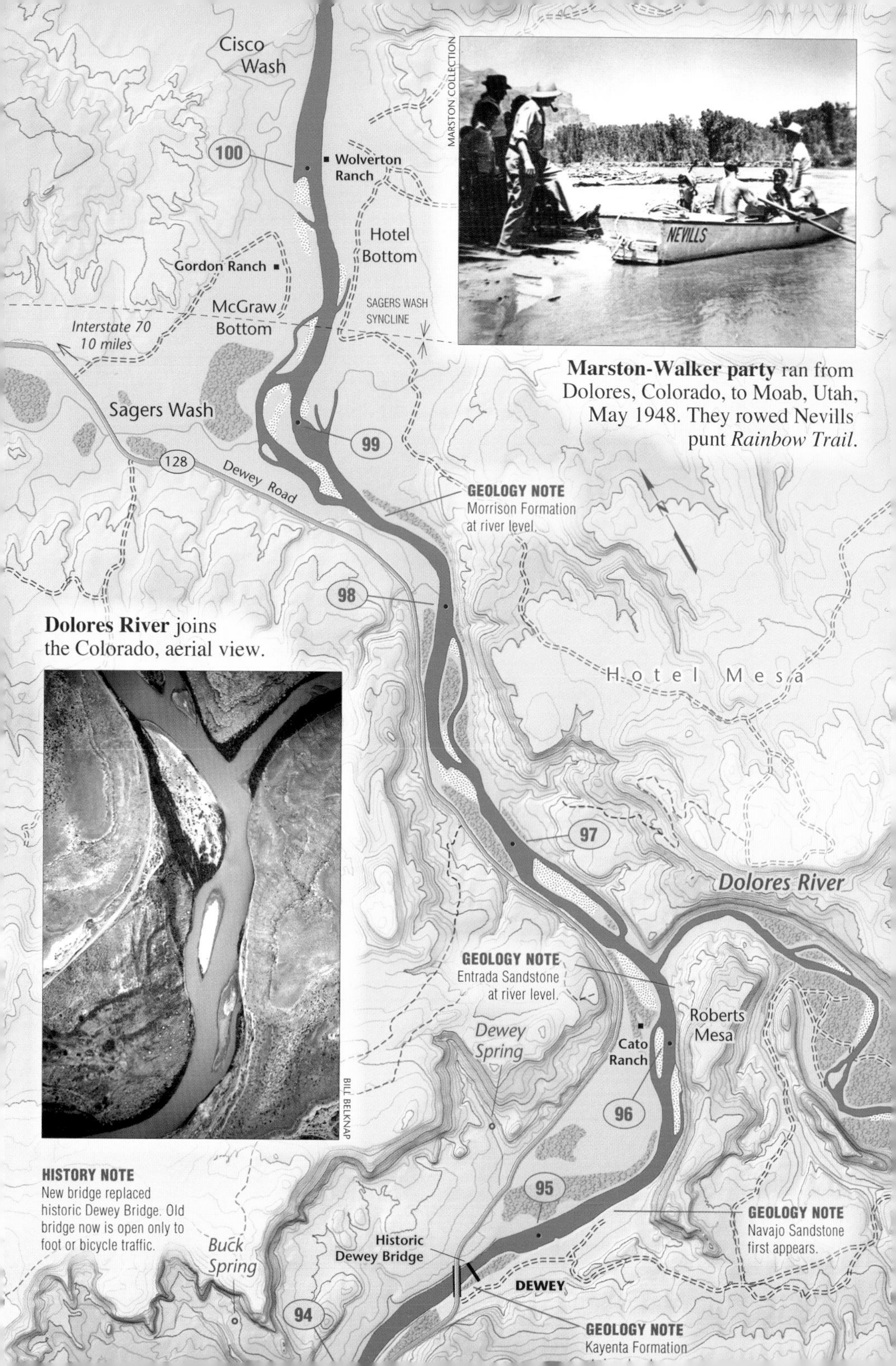

MARSTON COLLECTION

Marston-Walker party ran from Dolores, Colorado, to Moab, Utah, May 1948. They rowed Nevills punt *Rainbow Trail*.

Dolores River joins the Colorado, aerial view.

BILL BELKNAP

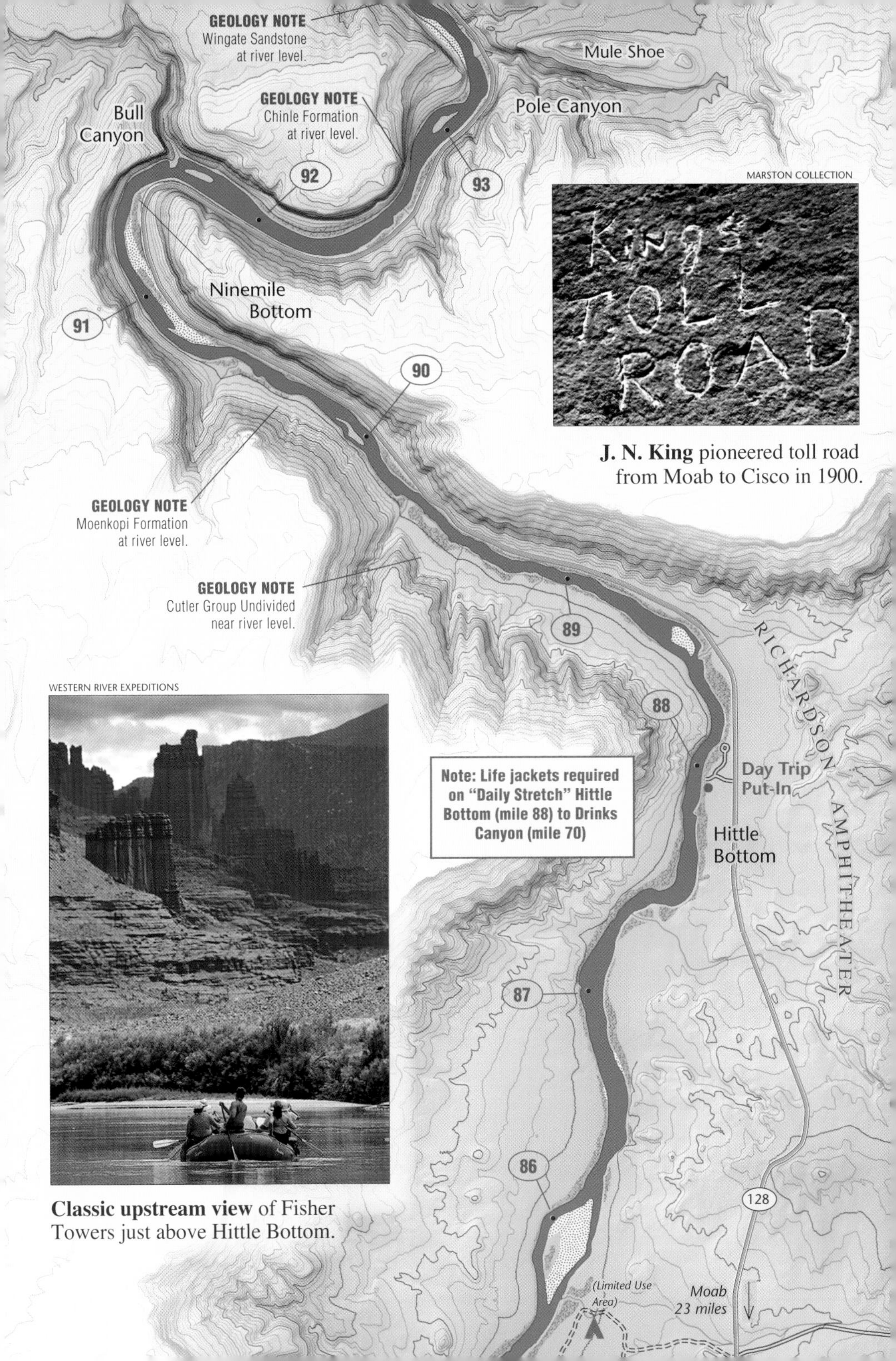

MARSTON COLLECTION

J. N. King pioneered toll road from Moab to Cisco in 1900.

WESTERN RIVER EXPEDITIONS

Classic upstream view of Fisher Towers just above Hittle Bottom.

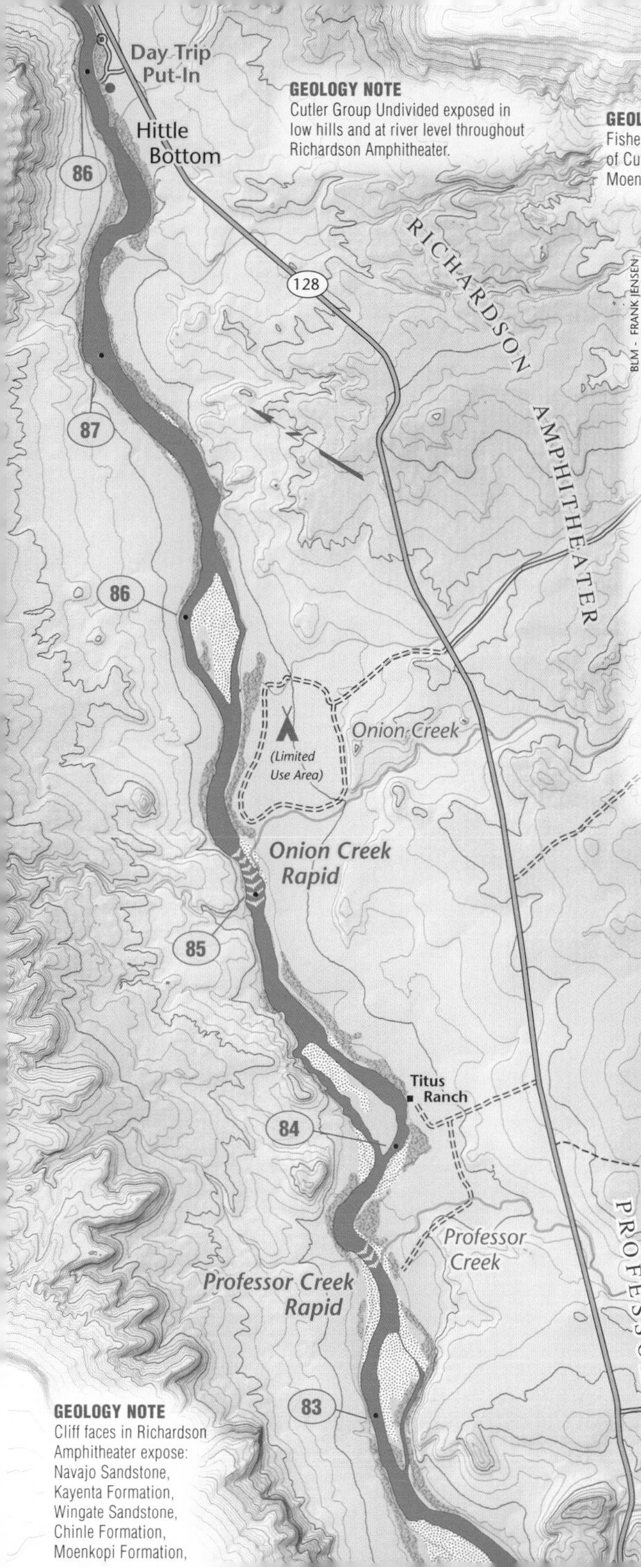

Day Trip Put-In
GEOLOGY NOTE
Cutler Group Undivided exposed in low hills and at river level throughout Richardson Amphitheater.
Hittle Bottom
86
GEOLOGY NOTE
Fisher Towers are generally composed of Cutler Group Undivided with a cap of Moenkopi Formation.
Fisher Towers
RICHARDSON AMPHITHEATER
128
87
86
Onion Creek
(Limited Use Area)
Onion Creek Rapid
85
Titus Ranch
84
PROFESSOR
Professor Creek
Professor Creek Rapid
83
GEOLOGY NOTE
Cliff faces in Richardson Amphitheater expose: Navajo Sandstone, Kayenta Formation, Wingate Sandstone, Chinle Formation, Moenkopi Formation,
Stearns Creek

BLM - FRANK JENSEN

Late afternoon sun enhances deep red of majestic **Fisher Towers.** *Below*, Bill Forrest tops nearby **Gothic Nightmare** in 1970 first ascent.

DON BRIGGS

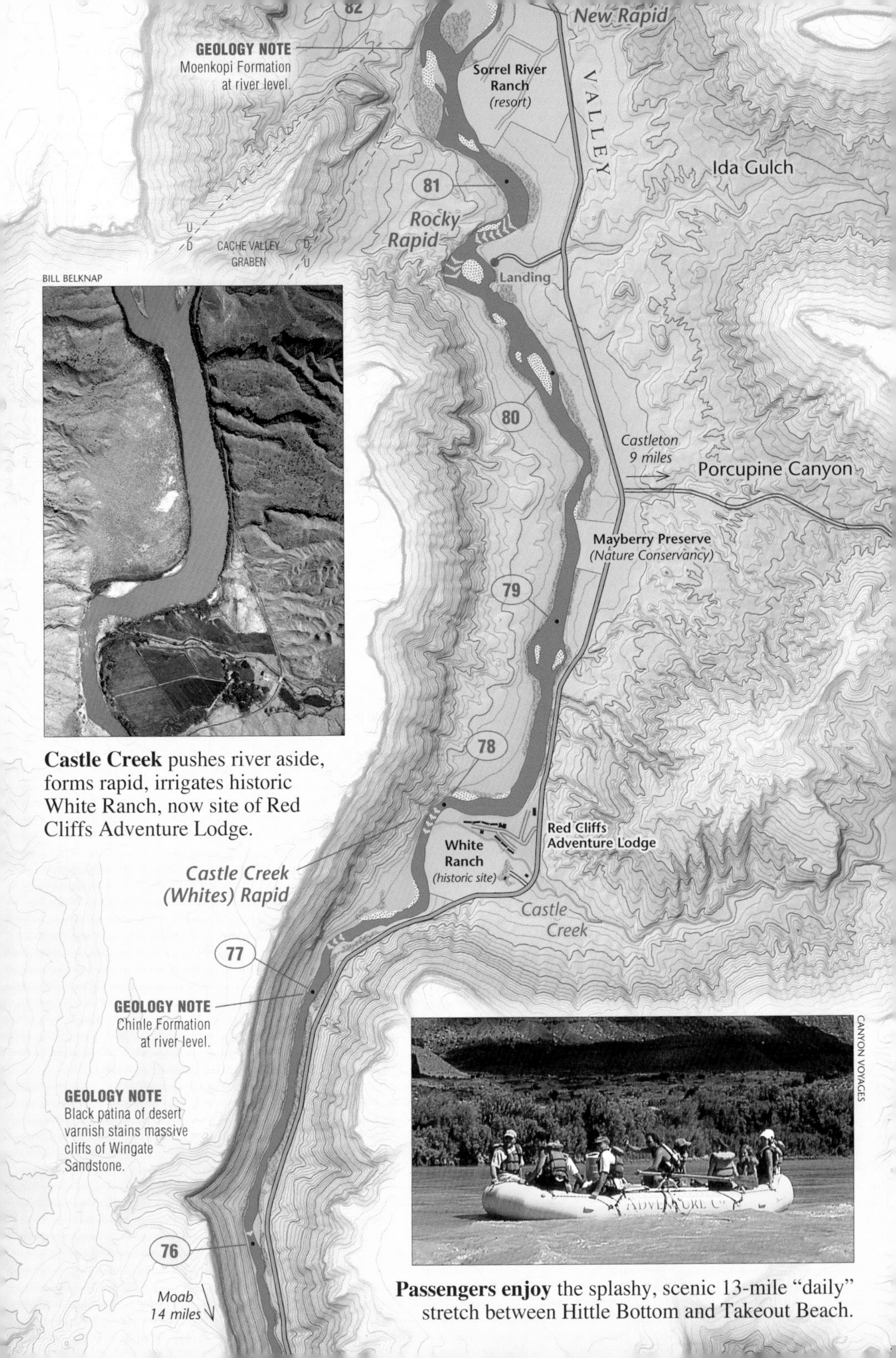
82
New Rapid
GEOLOGY NOTE
Moenkopi Formation at river level.
Sorrel River Ranch (resort)
VALLEY
Ida Gulch
81
Rocky Rapid
U
D
CACHE VALLEY GRABEN
D
U
Landing
BILL BELKNAP
80
Castleton 9 miles
Porcupine Canyon
Mayberry Preserve (Nature Conservancy)
79
Castle Creek pushes river aside, forms rapid, irrigates historic White Ranch, now site of Red Cliffs Adventure Lodge.
78
Red Cliffs Adventure Lodge
White Ranch (historic site)
Castle Creek (Whites) Rapid
Castle Creek
77
GEOLOGY NOTE
Chinle Formation at river level.
CANYON VOYAGES
GEOLOGY NOTE
Black patina of desert varnish stains massive cliffs of Wingate Sandstone.
76
Moab 14 miles
Passengers enjoy the splashy, scenic 13-mile "daily" stretch between Hittle Bottom and Takeout Beach.

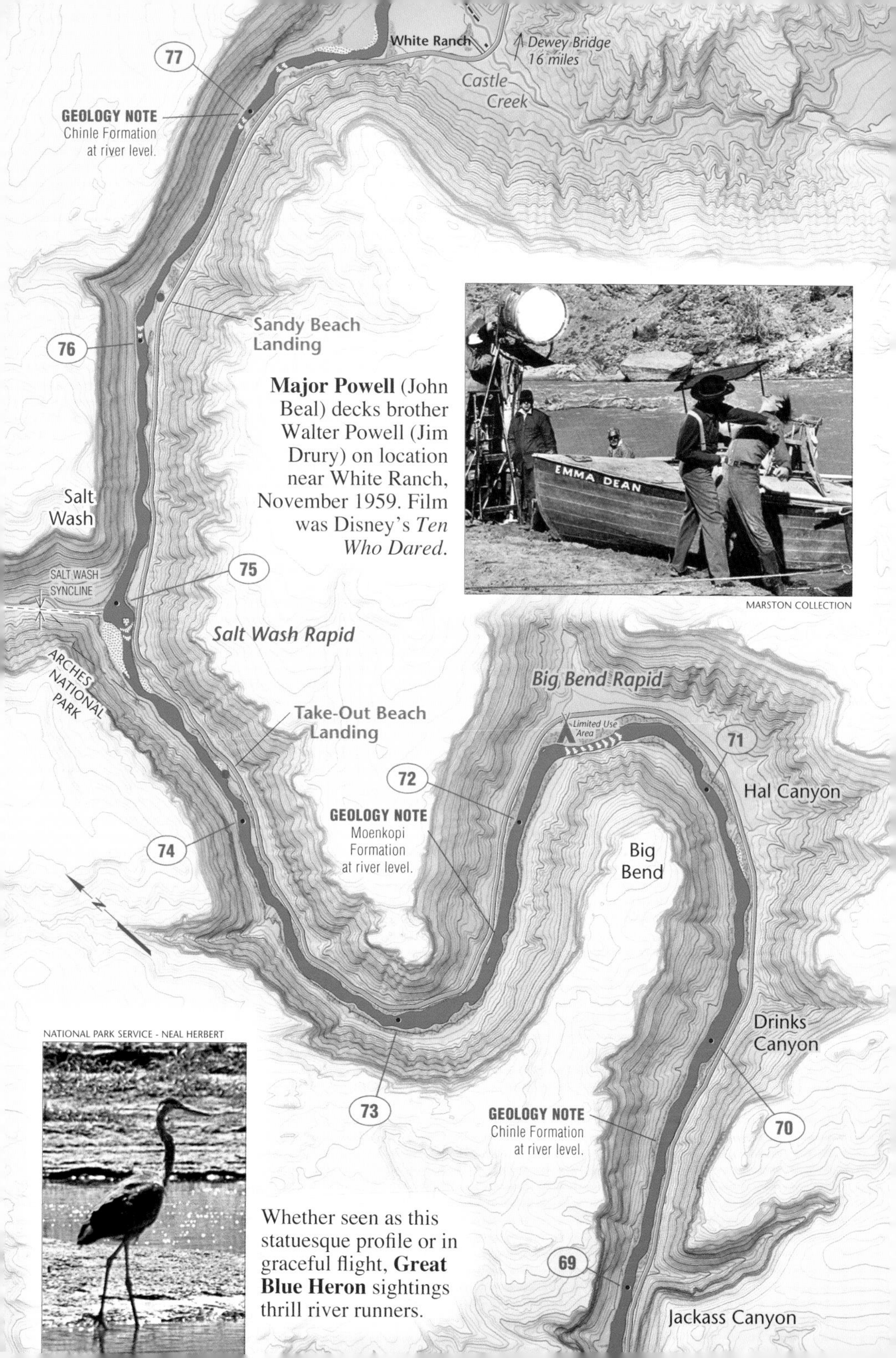

MARSTON COLLECTION

Major Powell (John Beal) decks brother Walter Powell (Jim Drury) on location near White Ranch, November 1959. Film was Disney's *Ten Who Dared.*

NATIONAL PARK SERVICE - NEAL HERBERT

Whether seen as this statuesque profile or in graceful flight, **Great Blue Heron** sightings thrill river runners.

M. WILLIAM ENGEL

TEX'S RIVERWAYS

Tex McClatchy built and skippered stern-wheeler *Canyon King* on Colorado near Moab. Boat is now used for scenic cruises and sunset dinners on Lake Powell.

Steamer *Undine*, built at Green River, capsized above Moab in 1901.

COURTESY CCRMA

computer colorized image

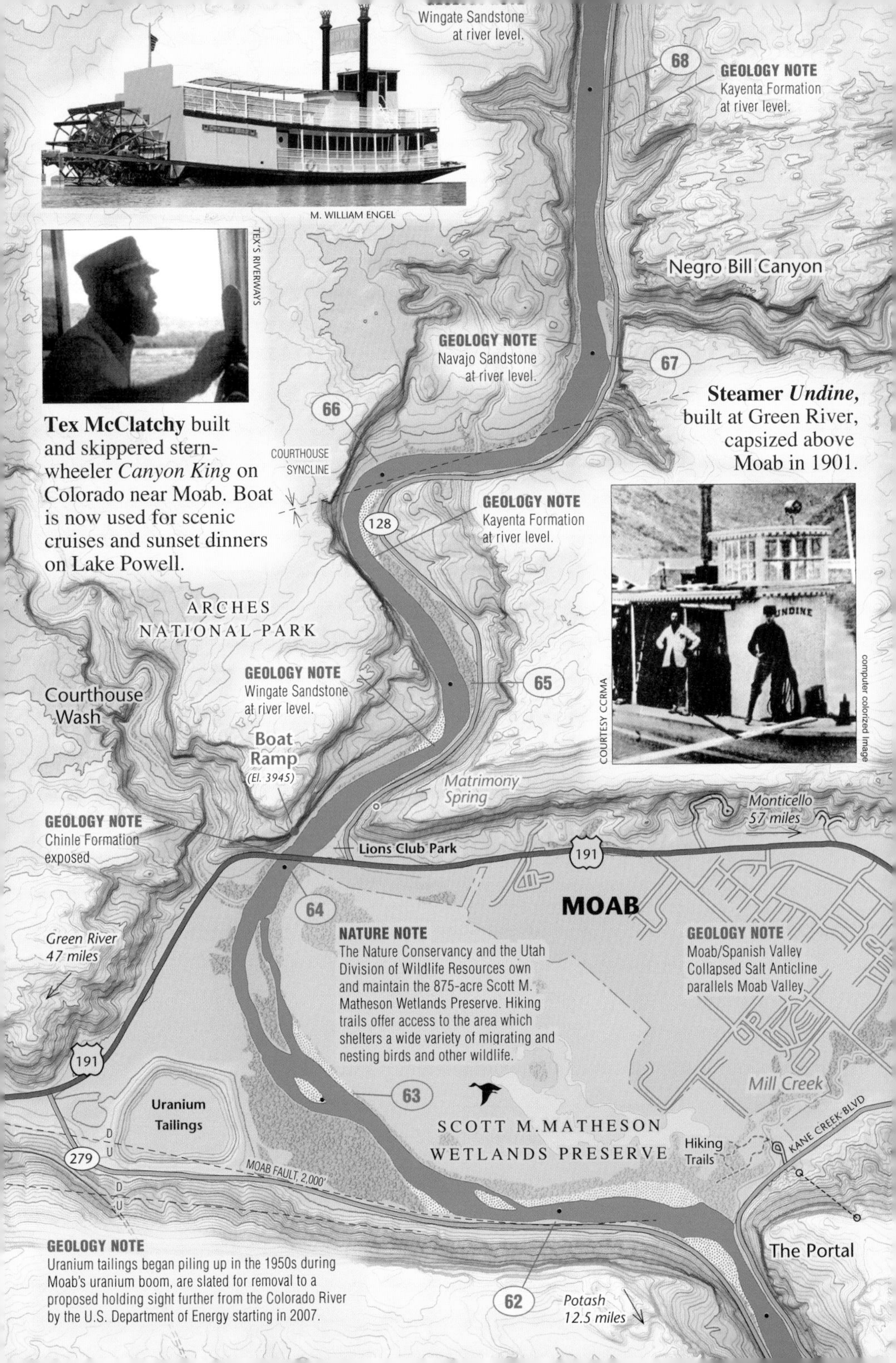

Wingate Sandstone at river level.
68
GEOLOGY NOTE
Kayenta Formation at river level.
Negro Bill Canyon
GEOLOGY NOTE
Navajo Sandstone at river level.
67
66
COURTHOUSE SYNCLINE
128
GEOLOGY NOTE
Kayenta Formation at river level.
ARCHES NATIONAL PARK
GEOLOGY NOTE
Wingate Sandstone at river level.
65
Courthouse Wash
Boat Ramp
(El. 3945)
Matrimony Spring
Monticello 57 miles
GEOLOGY NOTE
Chinle Formation exposed
Lions Club Park
191
64
MOAB
Green River 47 miles
NATURE NOTE
The Nature Conservancy and the Utah Division of Wildlife Resources own and maintain the 875-acre Scott M. Matheson Wetlands Preserve. Hiking trails offer access to the area which shelters a wide variety of migrating and nesting birds and other wildlife.
GEOLOGY NOTE
Moab/Spanish Valley Collapsed Salt Anticline parallels Moab Valley.
191
Mill Creek
63
Uranium Tailings
SCOTT M. MATHESON WETLANDS PRESERVE
Hiking Trails
KANE CREEK BLVD
279
D U
MOAB FAULT, 2,000'
D U
The Portal
GEOLOGY NOTE
Uranium tailings began piling up in the 1950s during Moab's uranium boom, are slated for removal to a proposed holding sight further from the Colorado River by the U.S. Department of Energy starting in 2007.
62
Potash 12.5 miles

MOAB – THE CONFLUENCE

Perhaps the most striking feature of this 64-mile stretch is its redness; heading downriver from Moab you soon wonder if the world has turned into red sandstone. Dense green thickets along the banks intensify the illusion.

To double your appreciation of a river trip, drive out to Dead Horse Point the afternoon before and watch the shadows lengthen over the Colorado and its incredible canyons.

On the river you'll find calm current and shifting sandbars down to Mile 1.5 where the channel narrows briefly at The Slide, causing some waves and turbulence.

The Park Service requires a permit for this stretch. For a list of outfitters offering trips on the section (and Cataract Canyon) write National Park Service, Canyonlands National Park, River District, 2282 S. West Resource Blvd., Moab, UT 84532. Phone: (435) 259-7164. Visit the Canyonlands National Park website at: www.nps.gov/cany.

Above photo: Colorado River from Dead Horse Point
BY BILL BELKNAP

RIVER FLOW INFORMATION
CALL: 801-539-1311 or go to www.cbrfc.noaa.gov/

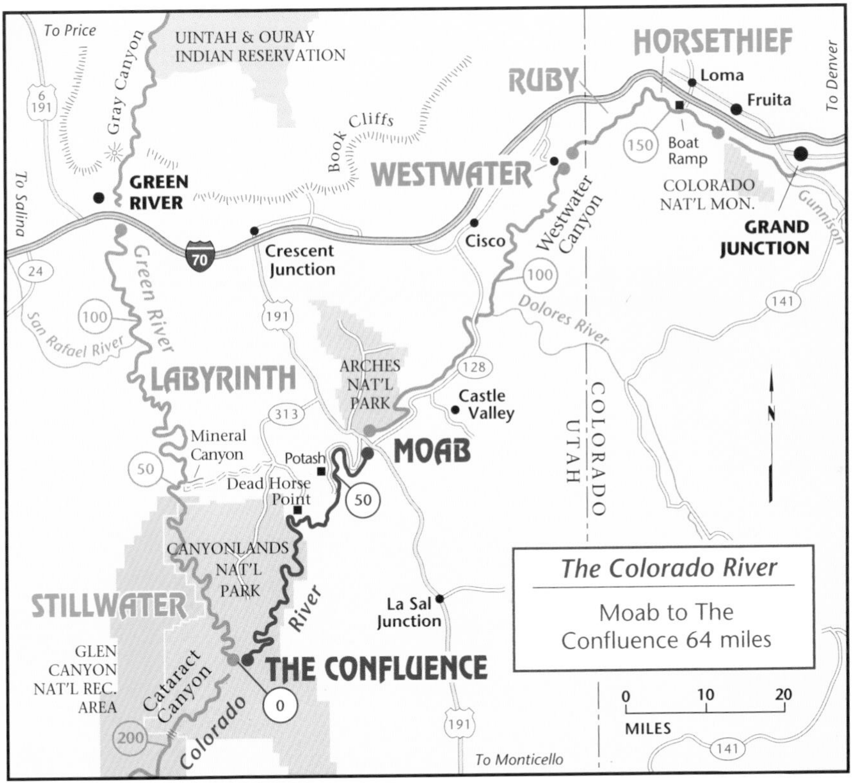

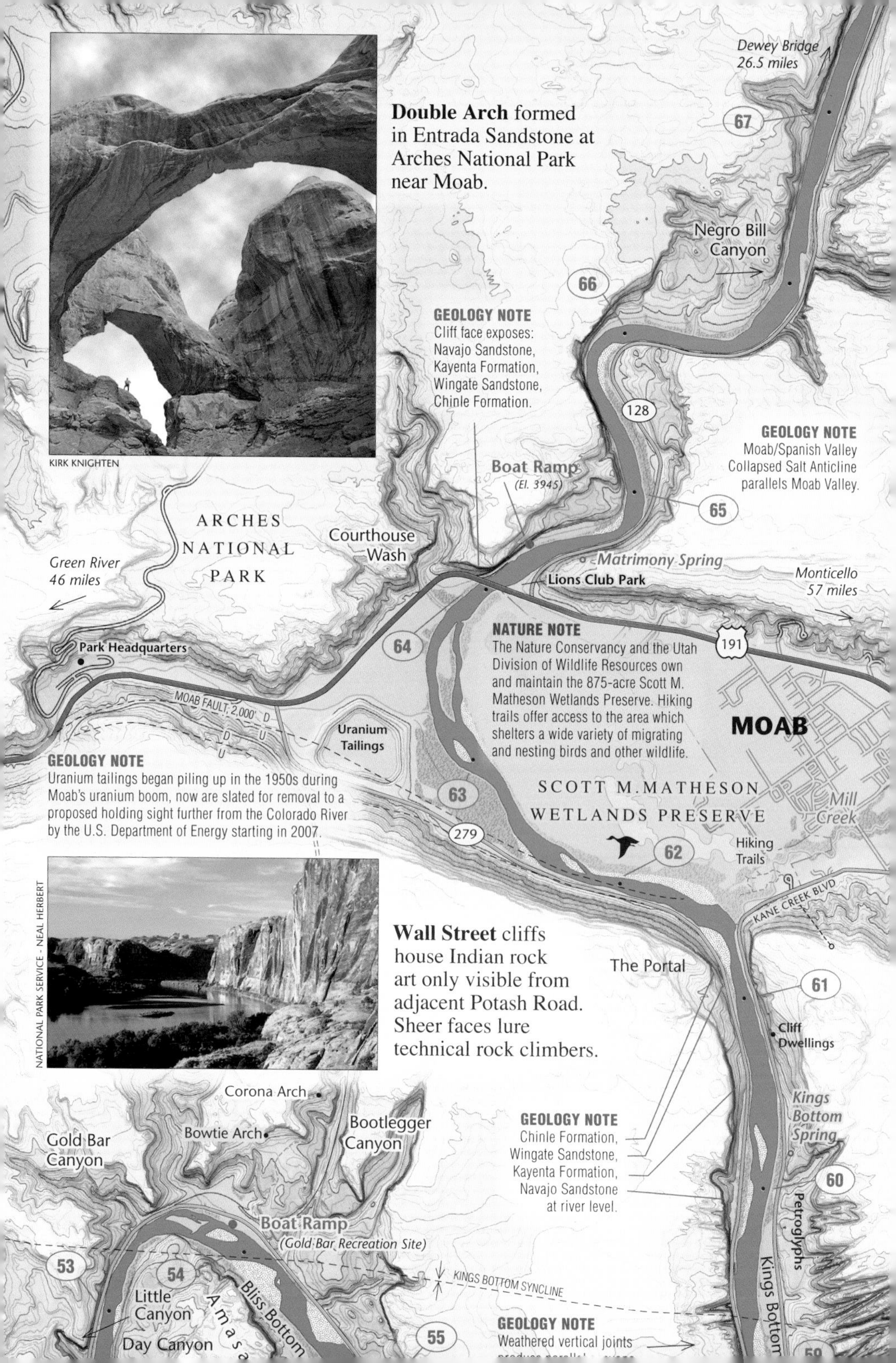

KIRK KNIGHTEN

Double Arch formed in Entrada Sandstone at Arches National Park near Moab.

GEOLOGY NOTE
Cliff face exposes: Navajo Sandstone, Kayenta Formation, Wingate Sandstone, Chinle Formation.

GEOLOGY NOTE
Moab/Spanish Valley Collapsed Salt Anticline parallels Moab Valley.

NATURE NOTE
The Nature Conservancy and the Utah Division of Wildlife Resources own and maintain the 875-acre Scott M. Matheson Wetlands Preserve. Hiking trails offer access to the area which shelters a wide variety of migrating and nesting birds and other wildlife.

GEOLOGY NOTE
Uranium tailings began piling up in the 1950s during Moab's uranium boom, now are slated for removal to a proposed holding sight further from the Colorado River by the U.S. Department of Energy starting in 2007.

NATIONAL PARK SERVICE - NEAL HERBERT

Wall Street cliffs house Indian rock art only visible from adjacent Potash Road. Sheer faces lure technical rock climbers.

GEOLOGY NOTE
Chinle Formation, Wingate Sandstone, Kayenta Formation, Navajo Sandstone at river level.

GEOLOGY NOTE
Weathered vertical joints

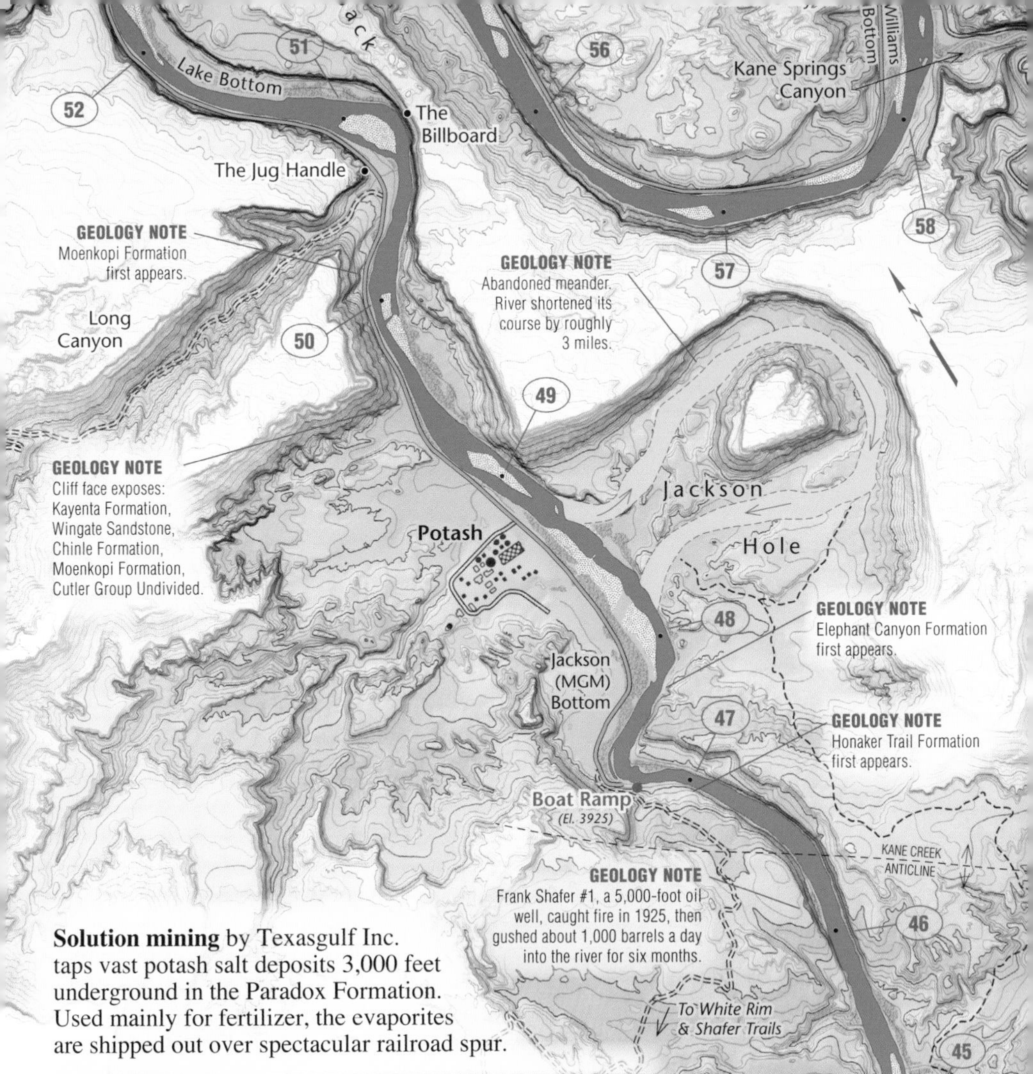

52
51
Lake Bottom
56
Kane Springs Canyon
Bottom
Williams
The Billboard
The Jug Handle
58
57
GEOLOGY NOTE
Moenkopi Formation first appears.
GEOLOGY NOTE
Abandoned meander. River shortened its course by roughly 3 miles.
Long Canyon
50
49
GEOLOGY NOTE
Cliff face exposes: Kayenta Formation, Wingate Sandstone, Chinle Formation, Moenkopi Formation, Cutler Group Undivided.
Potash
Jackson Hole
48
GEOLOGY NOTE
Elephant Canyon Formation first appears.
Jackson (MGM) Bottom
47
GEOLOGY NOTE
Honaker Trail Formation first appears.
Boat Ramp
(El. 3925)
KANE CREEK ANTICLINE
GEOLOGY NOTE
Frank Shafer #1, a 5,000-foot oil well, caught fire in 1925, then gushed about 1,000 barrels a day into the river for six months.
46
To White Rim & Shafer Trails
45
Shafer Basin
44
Salt Evaporators

Solution mining by Texasgulf Inc. taps vast potash salt deposits 3,000 feet underground in the Paradox Formation. Used mainly for fertilizer, the evaporites are shipped out over spectacular railroad spur.

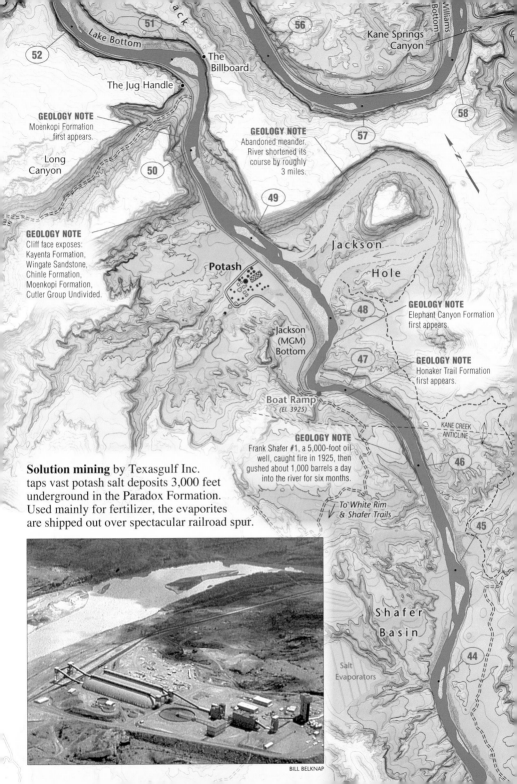

BILL BELKNAP

Moab 14 miles

LOIE EVANS

Thousands of tiny leaf beetles, *Diorhabda elongata*, tackle tenacious tamarisk, defoliating this invasive species in the Colorado River corridor. Recent biocontrol experiment (using natural enemies to help control pests) shows signs of success—miles of tamarisk are being decimated while native flora flourishes.

45

SYNCLINE

Shafer Basin

44

43

42

Pyramid Butte

41

N

39

40

NATIONAL PARK SERVICE - NEAL HERBERT

Common Raven

NATURE NOTE
Common Raven is a familiar sight on rim and river in Canyonlands country. Larger than a crow, it has a heavier bill, wedge shaped tail, and, at rest, a shaggy appearance at the throat. Often described as "opportunistic omnivores," ravens scavenge carrion, small rodents, and eggs, and happily cleanup leftovers from picnic areas and campsites. They often soar in flight like a hawk and delight in aerial displays of tumbling

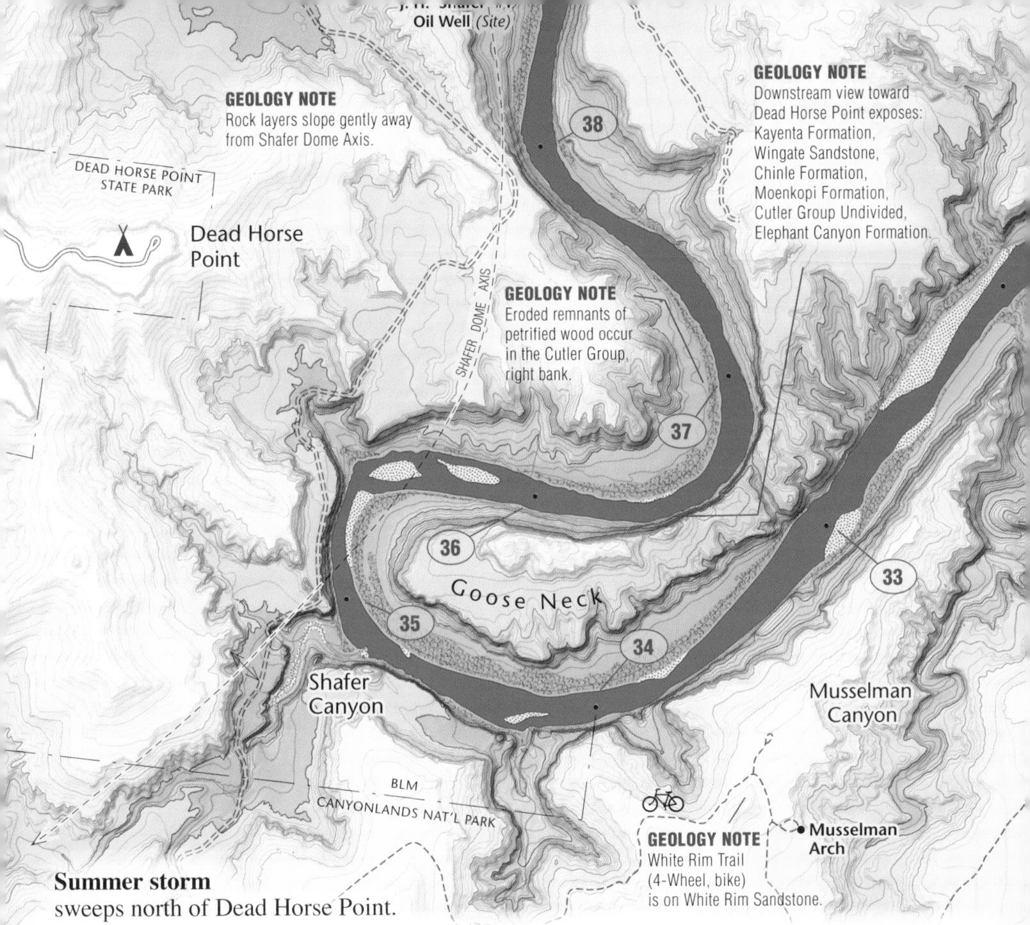
Oil Well (Site)
GEOLOGY NOTE
Rock layers slope gently away from Shafer Dome Axis.
GEOLOGY NOTE
Downstream view toward Dead Horse Point exposes: Kayenta Formation, Wingate Sandstone, Chinle Formation, Moenkopi Formation, Cutler Group Undivided, Elephant Canyon Formation.
DEAD HORSE POINT STATE PARK
Dead Horse Point
38
SHAFER DOME AXIS
GEOLOGY NOTE
Eroded remnants of petrified wood occur in the Cutler Group, right bank.
37
36
33
Goose Neck
35
34
Shafer Canyon
Musselman Canyon
BLM
CANYONLANDS NAT'L PARK
GEOLOGY NOTE
White Rim Trail (4-Wheel, bike) is on White Rim Sandstone.
Musselman Arch

Summer storm
sweeps north of Dead Horse Point.

BILL BELKNAP

NATIONAL PARK SERVICE - NEAL HERBERT

Collared lizard does pushup, ready to scoot.

BILL BELKNAP

White Rim points to river between Lathrop and Buck canyons. Hatch Point rises in background, Needles Overlook at right.

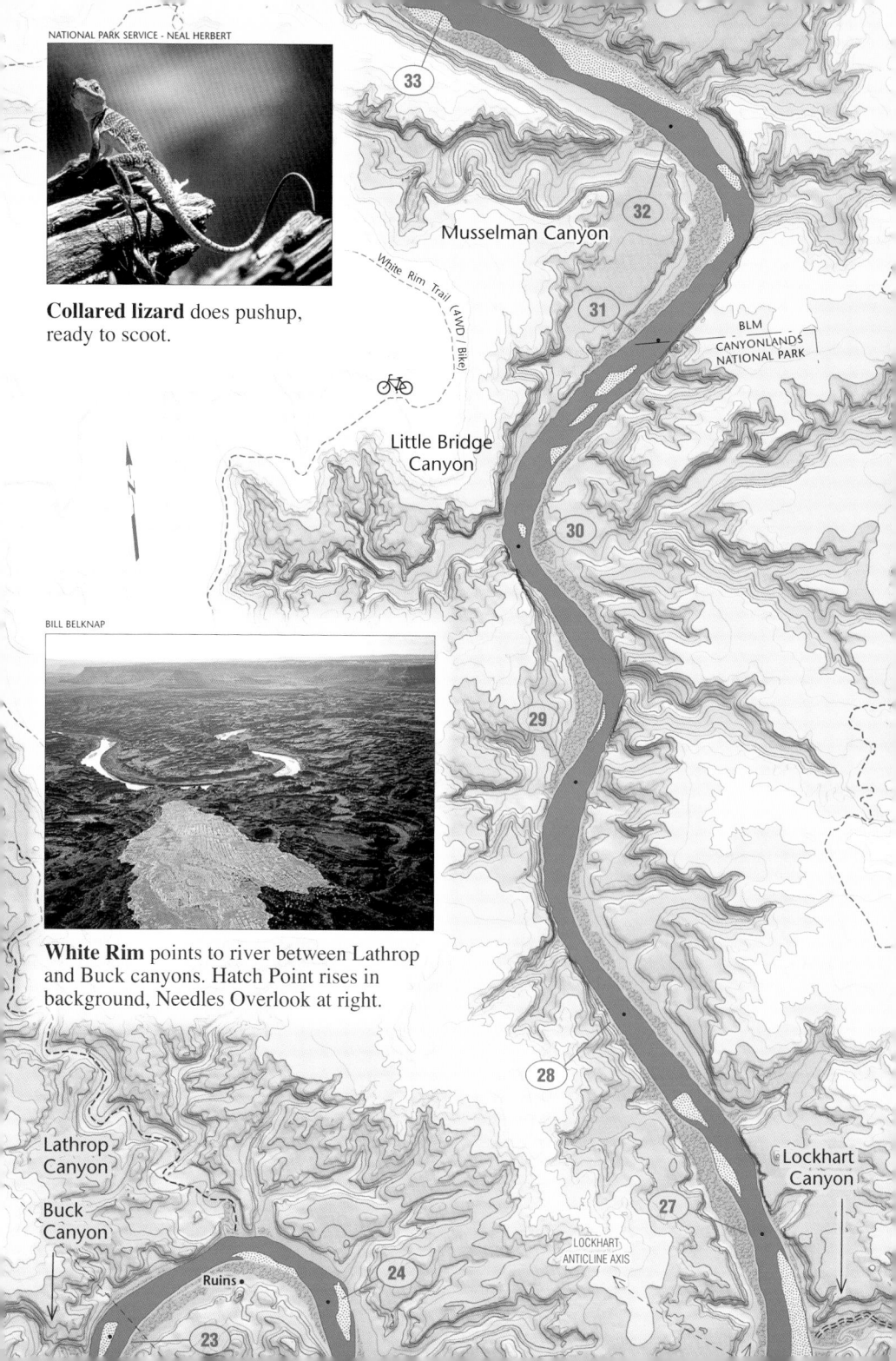

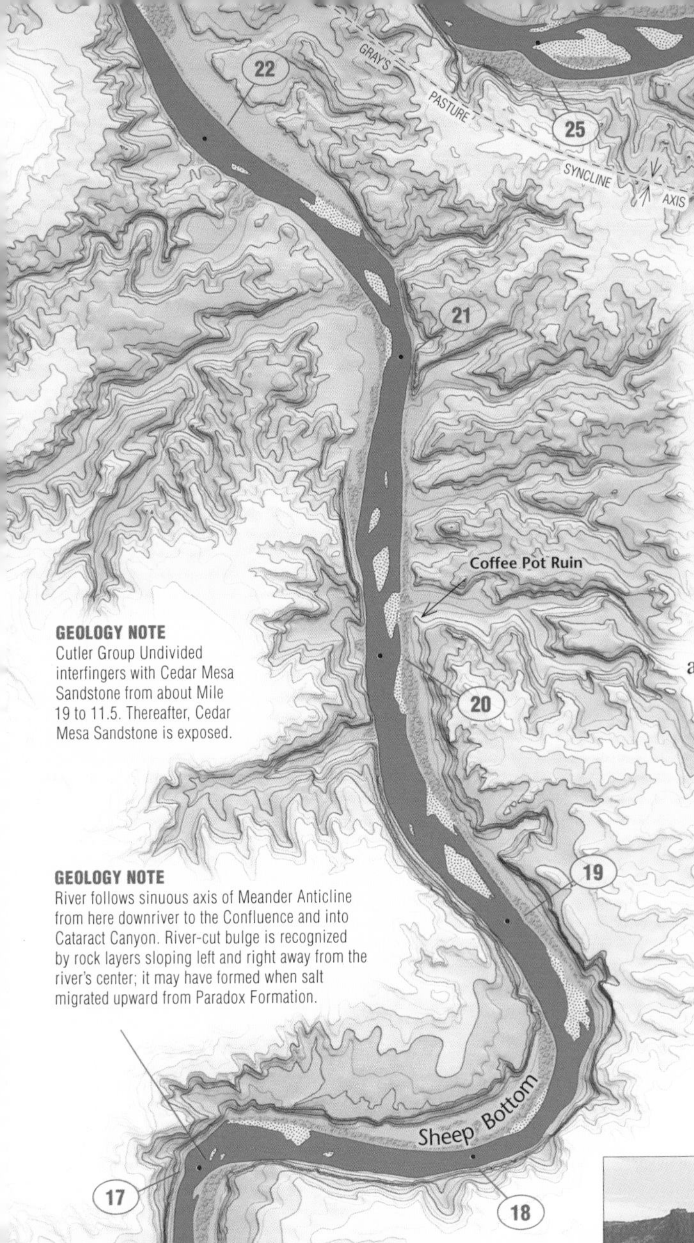

GEOLOGY NOTE
Cutler Group Undivided interfingers with Cedar Mesa Sandstone from about Mile 19 to 11.5. Thereafter, Cedar Mesa Sandstone is exposed.

GEOLOGY NOTE
River follows sinuous axis of Meander Anticline from here downriver to the Confluence and into Cataract Canyon. River-cut bulge is recognized by rock layers sloping left and right away from the river's center; it may have formed when salt migrated upward from Paradox Formation.

BILL BELKNAP

Cliff dwellings and primitive art (below) reward bushwhack through tamarisk across river from Lathrop Canyon.

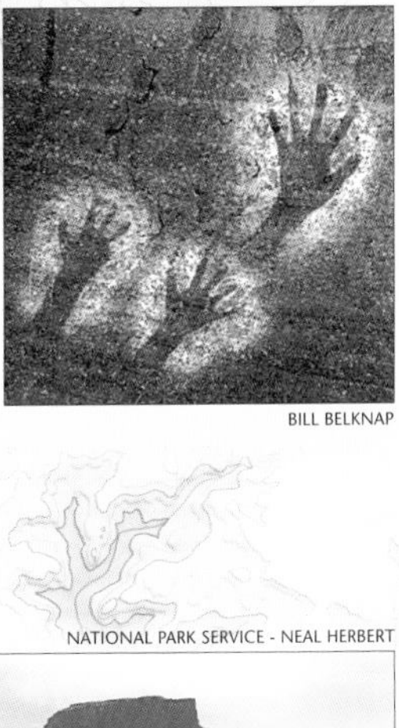

BILL BELKNAP

NATIONAL PARK SERVICE - NEAL HERBERT

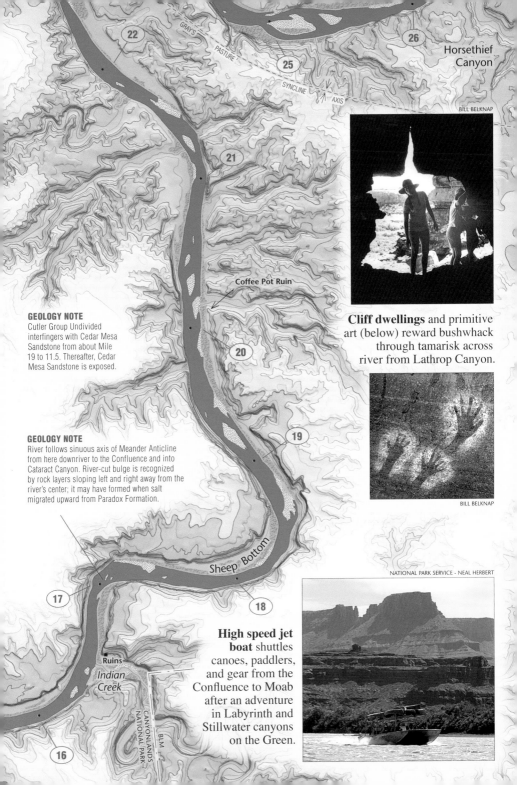

High speed jet boat shuttles canoes, paddlers, and gear from the Confluence to Moab after an adventure in Labyrinth and Stillwater canyons on the Green.

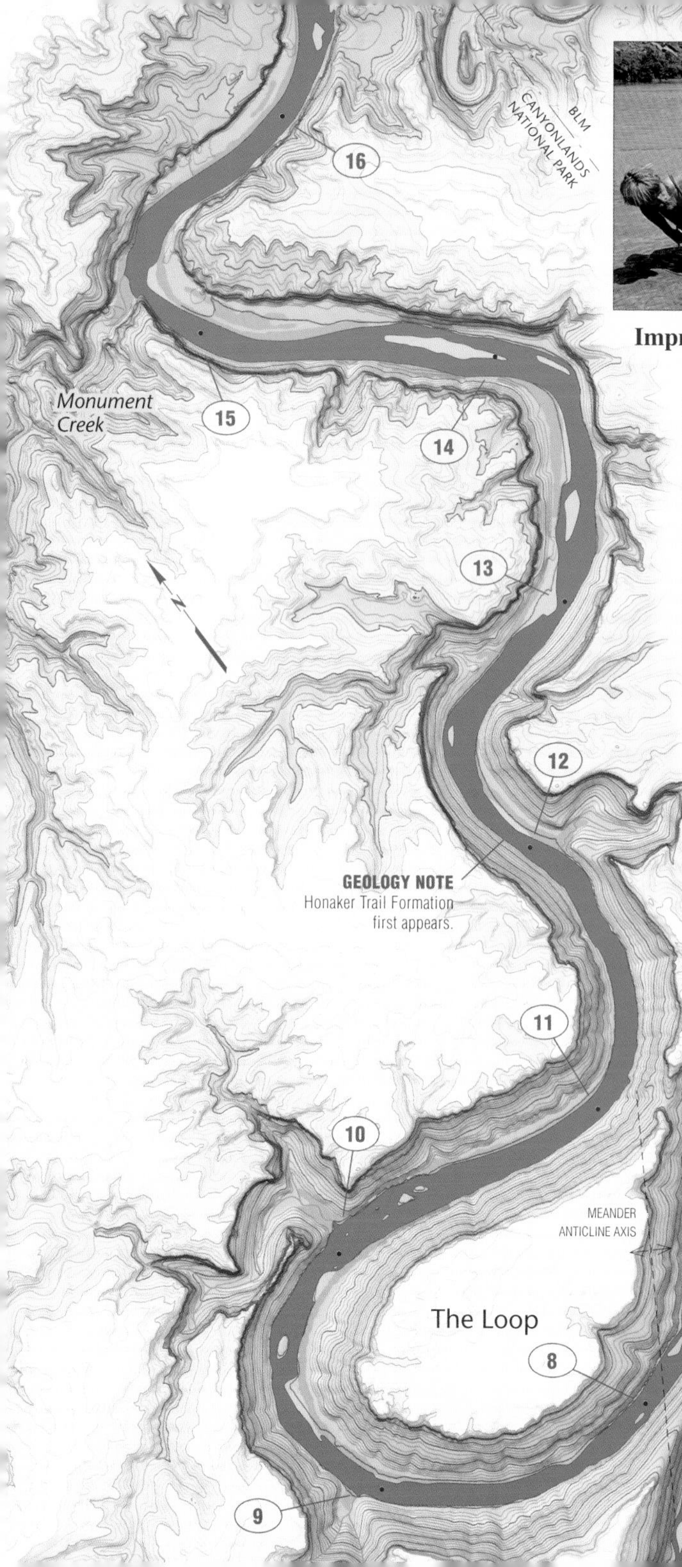

BILL BELKNAP

Impromptu trio rocks in quicksand.

NATIONAL PARK SERVICE - STEVE YOUNG

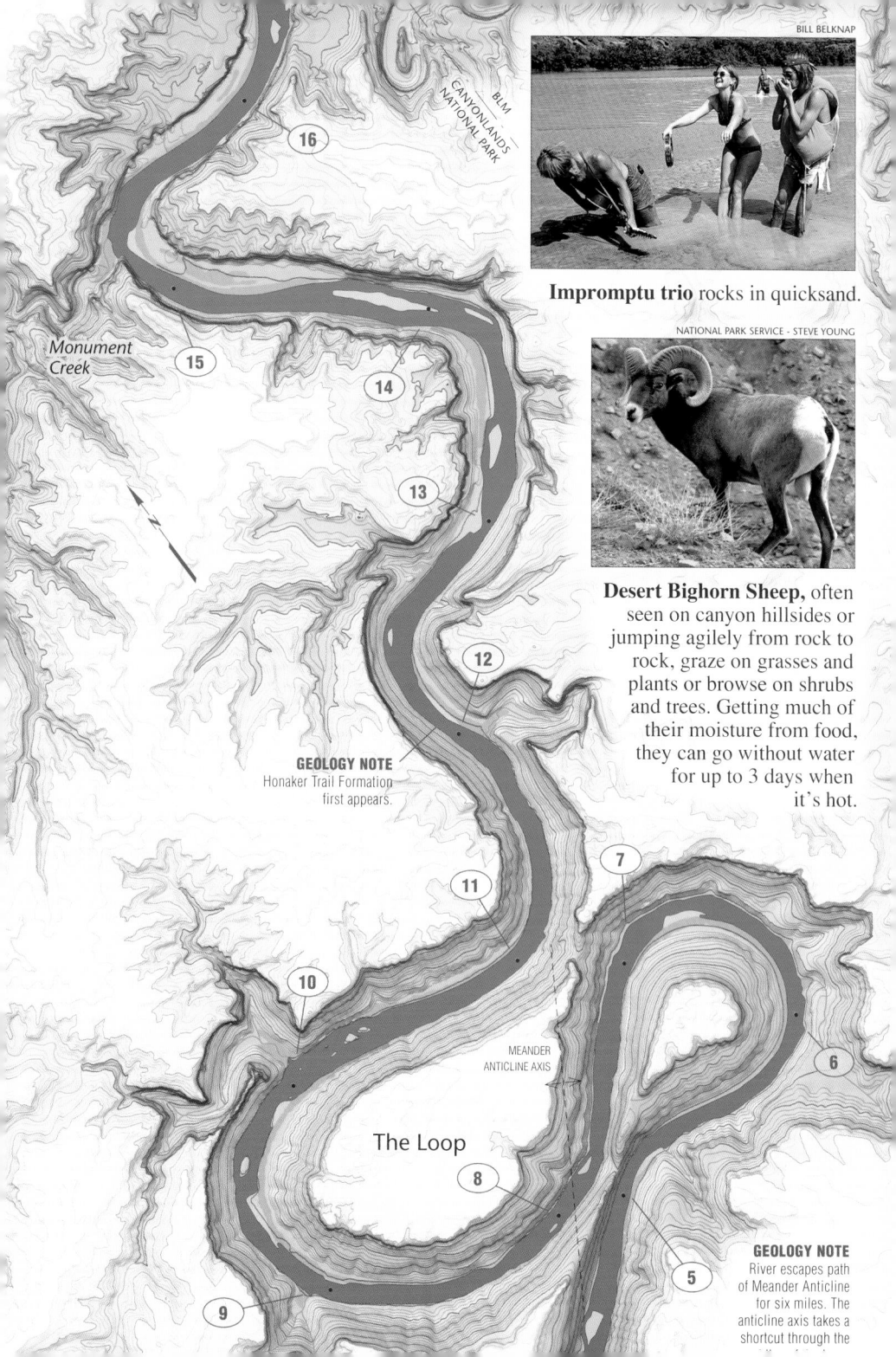

Desert Bighorn Sheep, often seen on canyon hillsides or jumping agilely from rock to rock, graze on grasses and plants or browse on shrubs and trees. Getting much of their moisture from food, they can go without water for up to 3 days when it's hot.

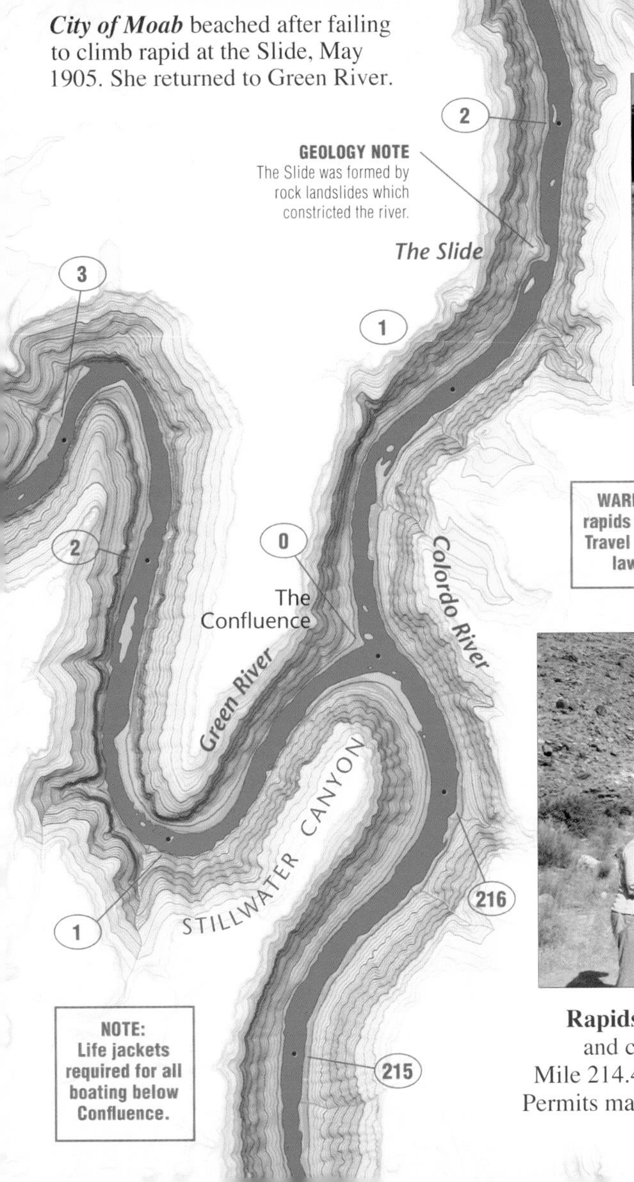

P. ELA MARSTON COLLECTION

City of Moab beached after failing to climb rapid at the Slide, May 1905. She returned to Green River.

GEOLOGY NOTE
The Slide was formed by rock landslides which constricted the river.

NATIONAL PARK SERVICE - NEAL HERBERT

Salt Creek flash flood muddies the Colorado.

WARNING: Dangerous rapids 4 miles downriver! Travel permit required by law. See page 61.

LOIE EVANS

Rapids ahead! National Park Service sign and courtesy campsite registration box at Mile 214.4 mark the head of Cataract Canyon. Permits mandatory; Campsite signup voluntary but highly recommended.

NOTE: Life jackets required for all boating below Confluence.

EXPEDITIONS

CATARACT CANYON

Cataract Canyon's rapids rank along with those of the Grand Canyon in power and difficulty, and they can become truly awe-inspiring during high water in May and June.

Rapids 21, 22, and 23 comprise The Big Drop, with a fall of 30 feet in less than a mile—one of the Colorado's steepest stretches.

In September 1921 United States Geological Survey engineer William R. Chenoweth surveyed and mapped the Colorado River through Cataract Canyon, numbered each rapid, and measured its fall. Since his rapid numbers have been widely accepted for more than 70 years, they are used in this book.

To traverse Cataract Canyon within Canyonlands National Park you must either go with an authorized guide or obtain your own permit. Write National Park Service, Canyonlands National Park, River District, 2282 S. West Resource Blvd., Moab, UT 84532 for a list of outfitters offering guided trips, or for private permit information. Phone: (434) 259-7164. Visit Canyonlands National Park website at: www.nps.gov/cany.

Above photo: Sweep oar powered "Triple Rig" drops into Big Drop, high water, early 1970s. BY BILL BELKNAP

RIVER FLOW INFORMATION
CALL: 801-539-1311 or go to www.cbrfc.noaa.gov/

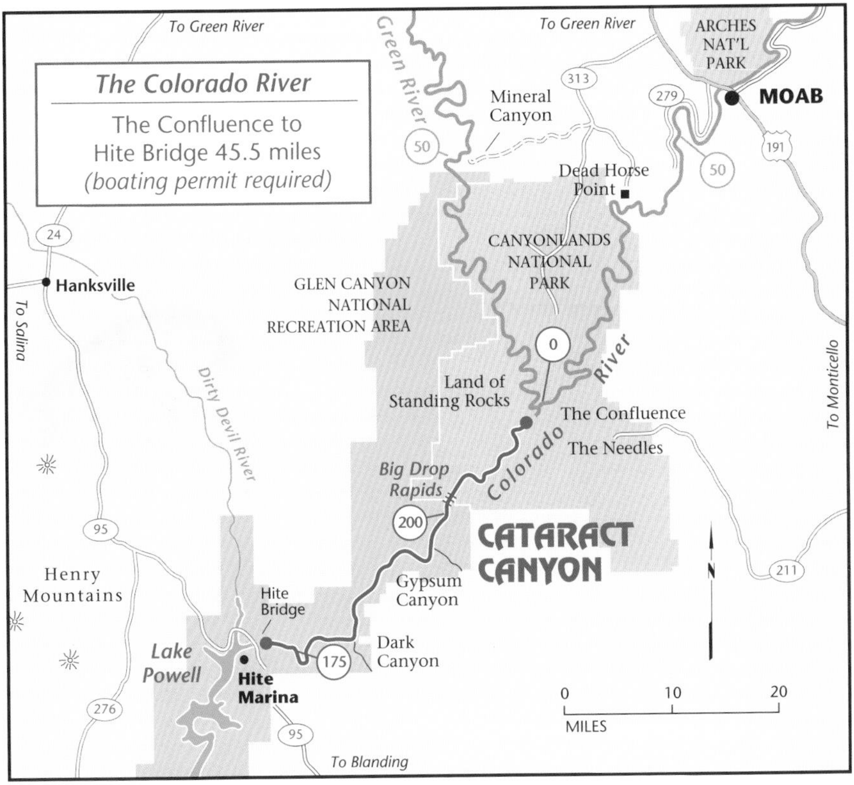

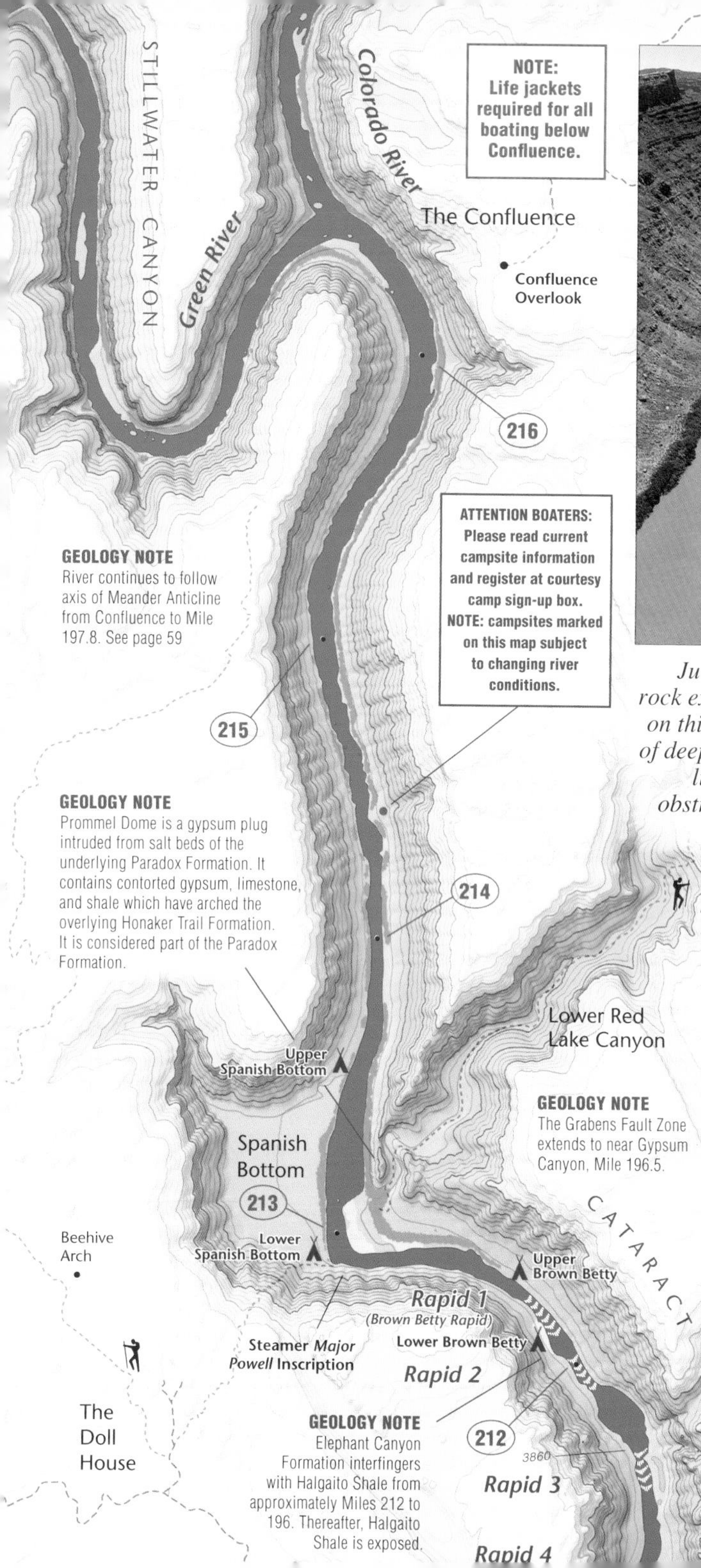
STILLWATER CANYON
Green River
Colorado River
NOTE: Life jackets required for all boating below Confluence.
The Confluence
Confluence Overlook
216
ATTENTION BOATERS: Please read current campsite information and register at courtesy camp sign-up box. NOTE: campsites marked on this map subject to changing river conditions.
GEOLOGY NOTE
River continues to follow axis of Meander Anticline from Confluence to Mile 197.8. See page 59
215
GEOLOGY NOTE
Prommel Dome is a gypsum plug intruded from salt beds of the underlying Paradox Formation. It contains contorted gypsum, limestone, and shale which have arched the overlying Honaker Trail Formation. It is considered part of the Paradox Formation.
214
Trail to Needles
Lower Red Lake Canyon
Upper Spanish Bottom
Spanish Bottom
213
GEOLOGY NOTE
The Grabens Fault Zone extends to near Gypsum Canyon, Mile 196.5.
CATARACT
Beehive Arch
Lower Spanish Bottom
Upper Brown Betty
Rapid 1
(Brown Betty Rapid)
Steamer Major Powell Inscription
Lower Brown Betty
Rapid 2
The Doll House
GEOLOGY NOTE
Elephant Canyon Formation interfingers with Halgaito Shale from approximately Miles 212 to 196. Thereafter, Halgaito Shale is exposed.
212
3860
Rapid 3
Rapid 4

BILL BELKNAP

July 20, 1869 — "A long neck of rock extends toward the Grand. Out on this we walk, crossing a number of deep crevices. It is curious how a little obstacle becomes a great obstruction when a misstep would land a man in a deep chasm.

J.W. Powell

Powell Report

MARSTON COLLECTION

Steamer *Major Powell* made two round trips from San Rafael River to Spanish Bottom. Fading inscription marks her turnaround March 24, 1893.

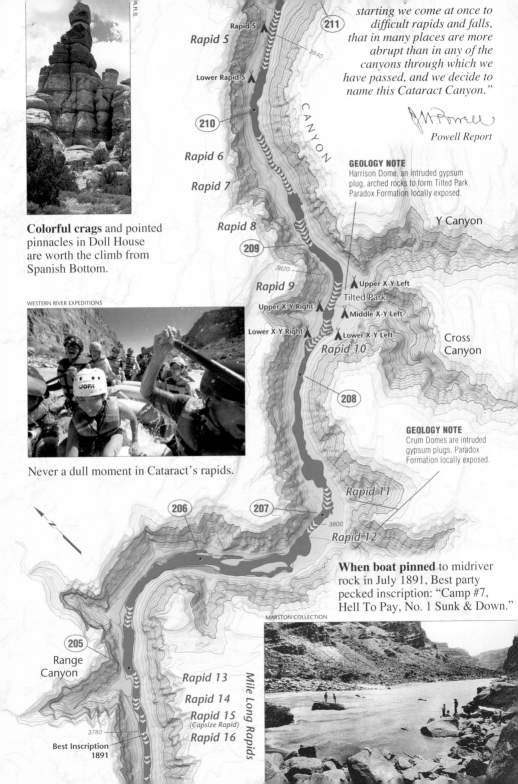

starting we come at once to difficult rapids and falls, that in many places are more abrupt than in any of the canyons through which we have passed, and we decide to name this Cataract Canyon."

J.W. Powell

Powell Report

A.R.S.

Colorful crags and pointed pinnacles in Doll House are worth the climb from Spanish Bottom.

WESTERN RIVER EXPEDITIONS

Never a dull moment in Cataract's rapids.

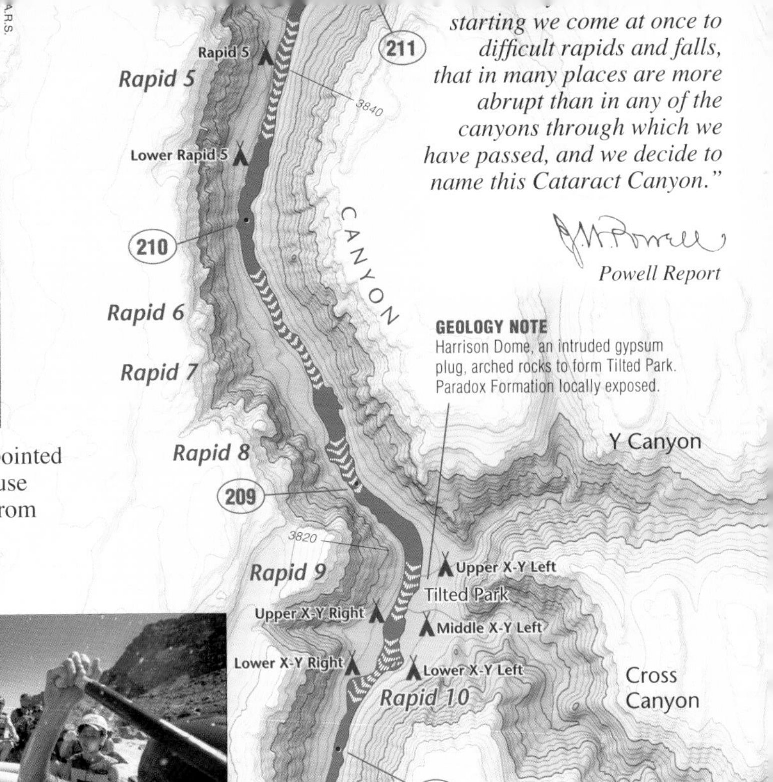

GEOLOGY NOTE
Harrison Dome, an intruded gypsum plug, arched rocks to form Tilted Park. Paradox Formation locally exposed.

GEOLOGY NOTE
Crum Domes are intruded gypsum plugs. Paradox Formation locally exposed.

When boat pinned to midriver rock in July 1891, Best party pecked inscription: "Camp #7, Hell To Pay, No. 1 Sunk & Down."

MARSTON COLLECTION

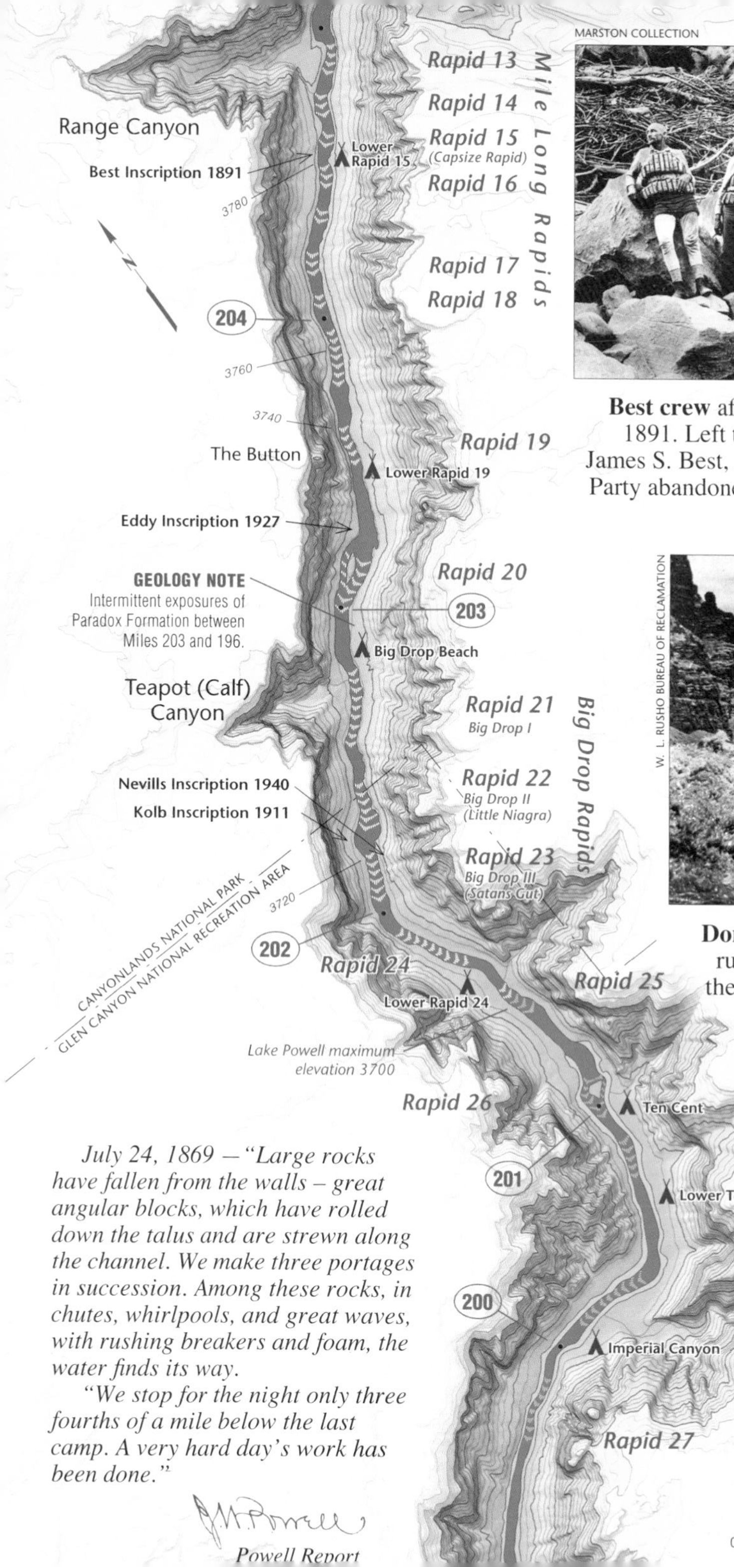

MARSTON COLLECTION

Best crew after losing boat on July 22, 1891. Left to right: Harry McDonald, James S. Best, J. W. Jewell, Elmer Kane. Party abandoned prospecting effort after limping on to Lees Ferry.

W. L. RUSHO BUREAU OF RECLAMATION

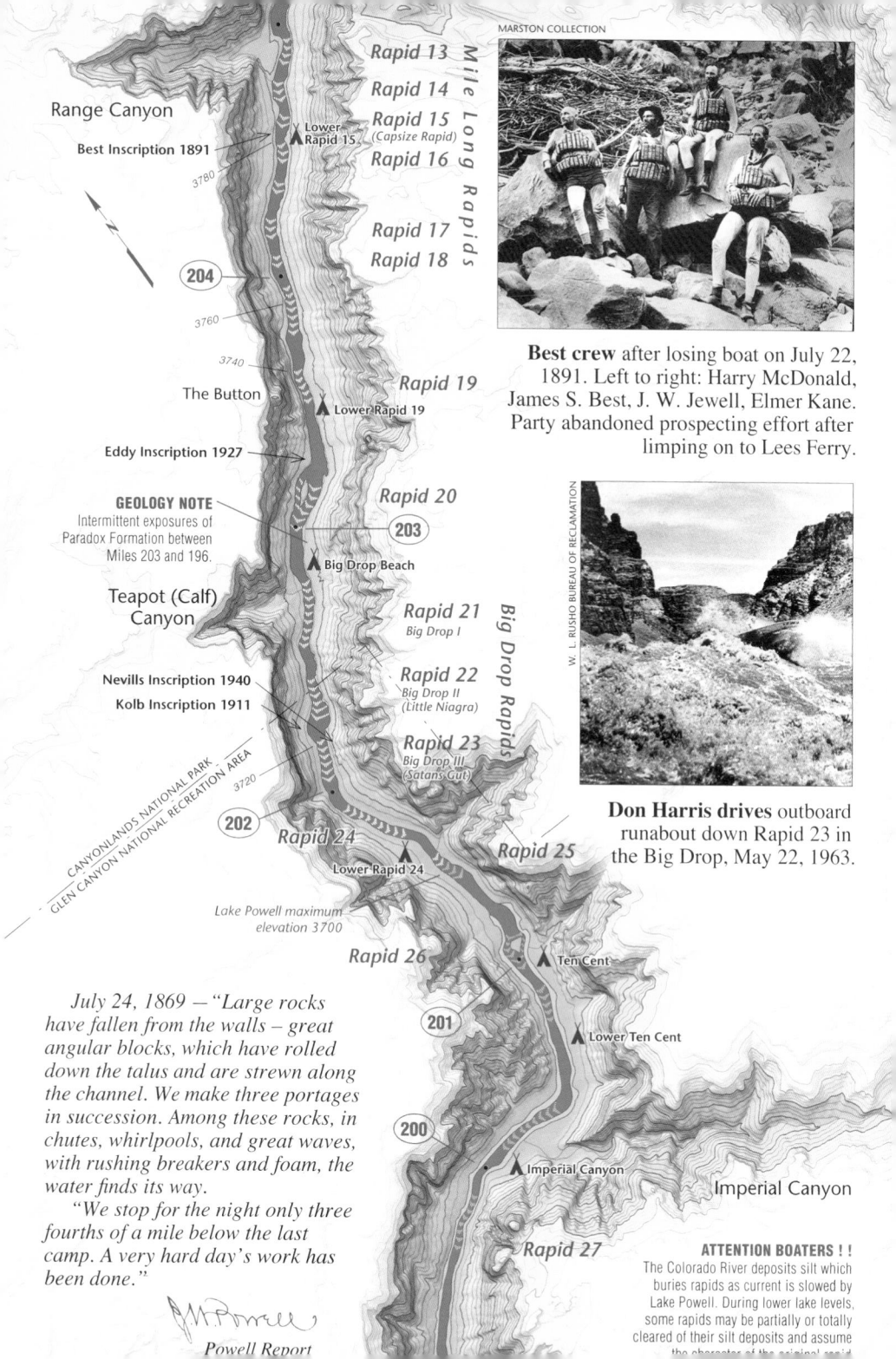

Don Harris drives outboard runabout down Rapid 23 in the Big Drop, May 22, 1963.

July 24, 1869 — "Large rocks have fallen from the walls – great angular blocks, which have rolled down the talus and are strewn along the channel. We make three portages in succession. Among these rocks, in chutes, whirlpools, and great waves, with rushing breakers and foam, the water finds its way.

"We stop for the night only three fourths of a mile below the last camp. A very hard day's work has been done."

J.W. Powell

Powell Report

ATTENTION BOATERS ! !
The Colorado River deposits silt which buries rapids as current is slowed by Lake Powell. During lower lake levels, some rapids may be partially or totally cleared of their silt deposits and assume

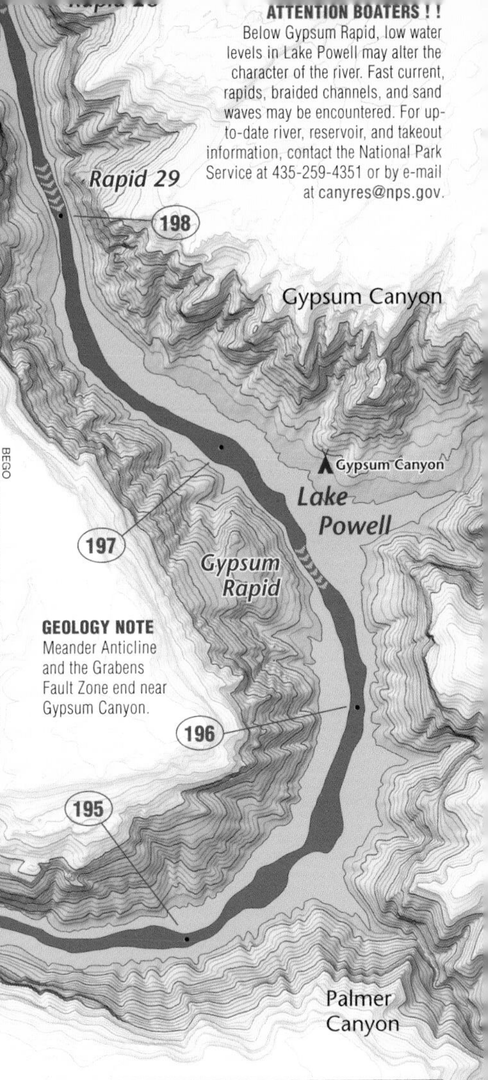

ATTENTION BOATERS ! !
Below Gypsum Rapid, low water levels in Lake Powell may alter the character of the river. Fast current, rapids, braided channels, and sand waves may be encountered. For up-to-date river, reservoir, and takeout information, contact the National Park Service at 435-259-4351 or by e-mail at canyres@nps.gov.

RSTON COLLECTION

The Big Drop, Rapid 23, paddled by Ken Ross and Bill Dickinson September 4, 1949.

NOTE:
Life jackets required until last active rapid. (Highly recommended to takeout.)

BEGO

Dory runs Big Drop Rapids on high water of 80,000 c.f.s., June 1983.

GEOLOGY NOTE
Meander Anticline and the Grabens Fault Zone end near Gypsum Canyon.

— NOTE —
Camping on Lake Powell is first come, first serve.

O.A.R.S.

Spacious, scenic campsite in lower Cataract Canyon.

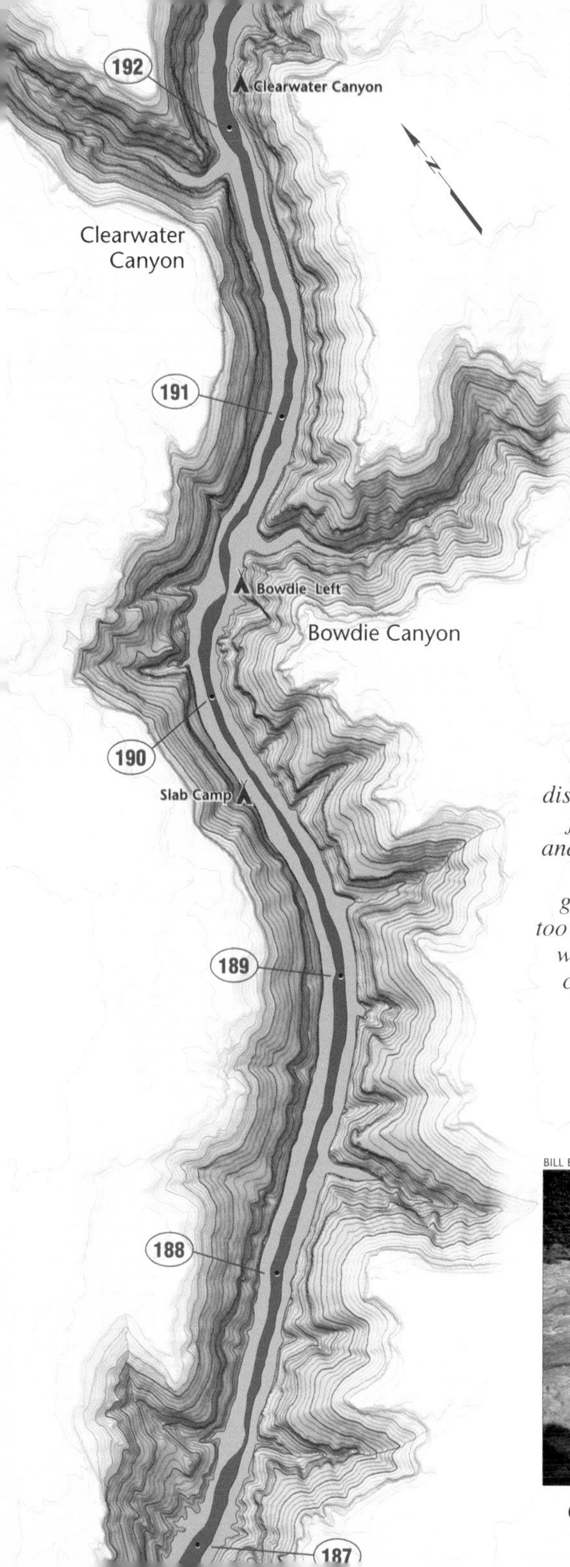

BILL BELKNAP

Clearwater Canyon's incised meanders snake toward the Colorado.

July 27, 1869 – "Late in the afternoon we discover a flock of mountain sheep a hundred feet above us. We land quickly, out of sight, and away go the hunters. Soon we hear firing.

"We lash our prizes to the deck and go on for a short distance; but fresh meat is too tempting, and we stop to have a feast. And what a feast it is! Two fine young sheep! We care not for bread or beans or dried apples tonight; coffee and mutton are all we ask."

Powell Report

BILL BELKNAP

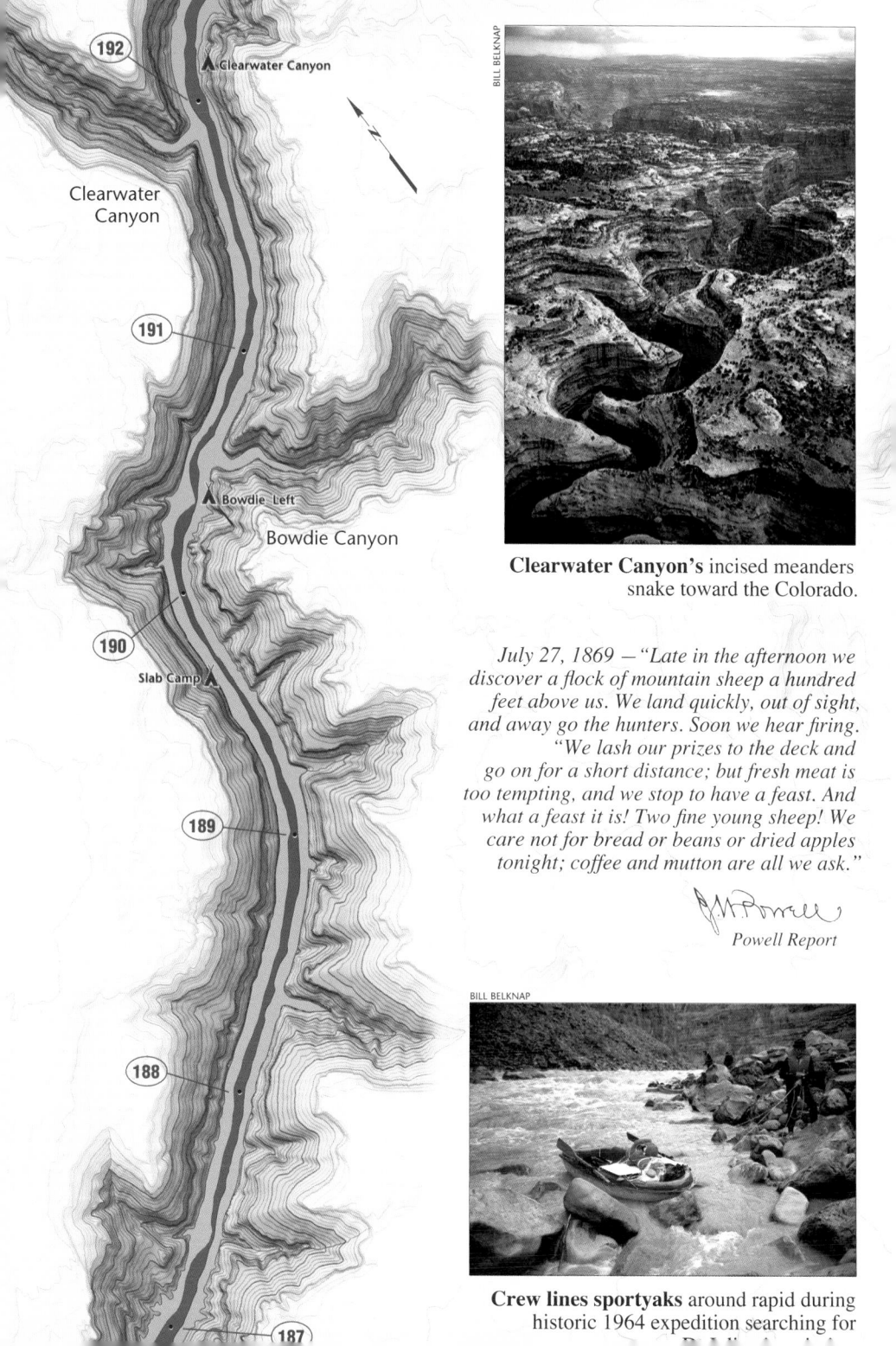

Crew lines sportyaks around rapid during historic 1964 expedition searching for

186
D. Julien Inscription
1836 *(Submerged)*
185
Cove Canyon
Rockfall Canyon
Rock Fall Mouth
184
Rock Fall Right
Dark Canyon
Dark Canyon Mouth
183
182
181
180

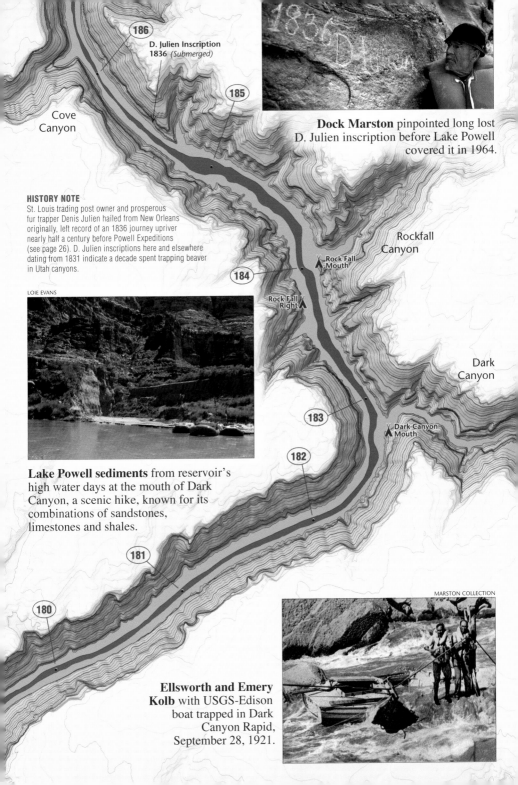

Dock Marston pinpointed long lost D. Julien inscription before Lake Powell covered it in 1964.

HISTORY NOTE

St. Louis trading post owner and prosperous fur trapper Denis Julien hailed from New Orleans originally, left record of an 1836 journey upriver nearly half a century before Powell Expeditions (see page 26). D. Julien inscriptions here and elsewhere dating from 1831 indicate a decade spent trapping beaver in Utah canyons.

LOIE EVANS

Lake Powell sediments from reservoir's high water days at the mouth of Dark Canyon, a scenic hike, known for its combinations of sandstones, limestones and shales.

MARSTON COLLECTION

Ellsworth and Emery Kolb with USGS-Edison boat trapped in Dark Canyon Rapid, September 28, 1921.

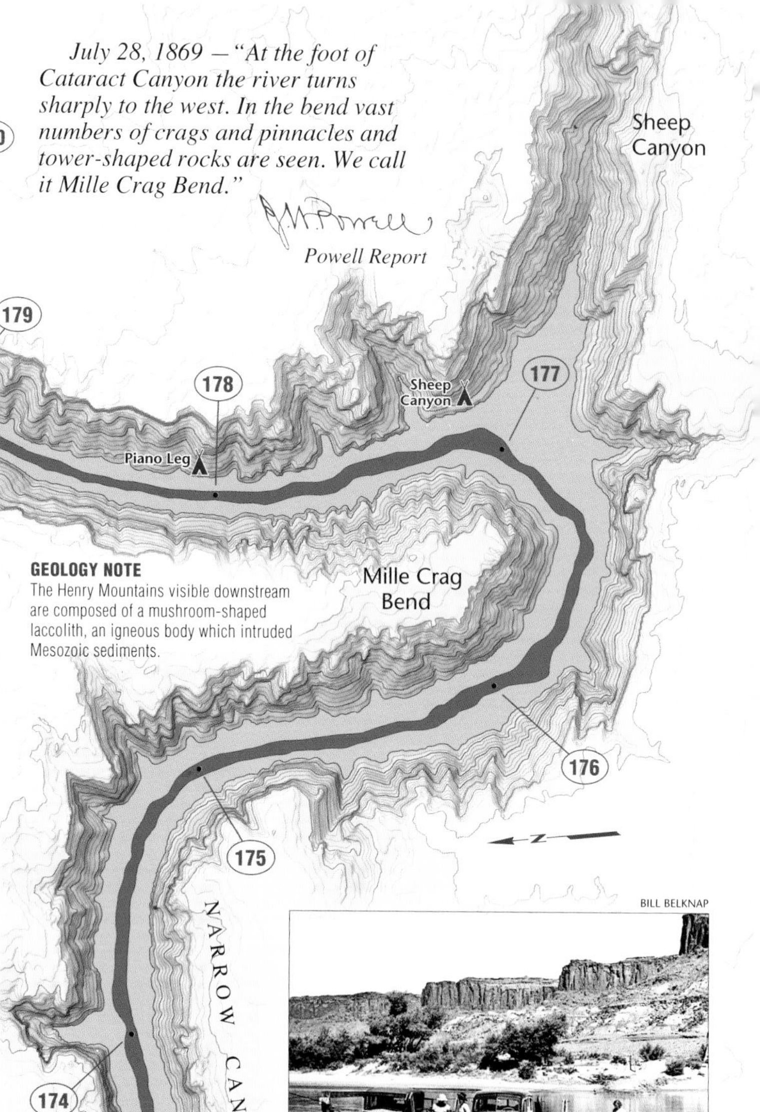

July 28, 1869 — "At the foot of Cataract Canyon the river turns sharply to the west. In the bend vast numbers of crags and pinnacles and tower-shaped rocks are seen. We call it Mille Crag Bend."

J.W. Powell

Powell Report

GEOLOGY NOTE
The Henry Mountains visible downstream are composed of a mushroom-shaped laccolith, an igneous body which intruded Mesozoic sediments.

BILL BELKNAP

Woman climber rappels from Hite Bridge to meet river party.

BILL BELKNAP

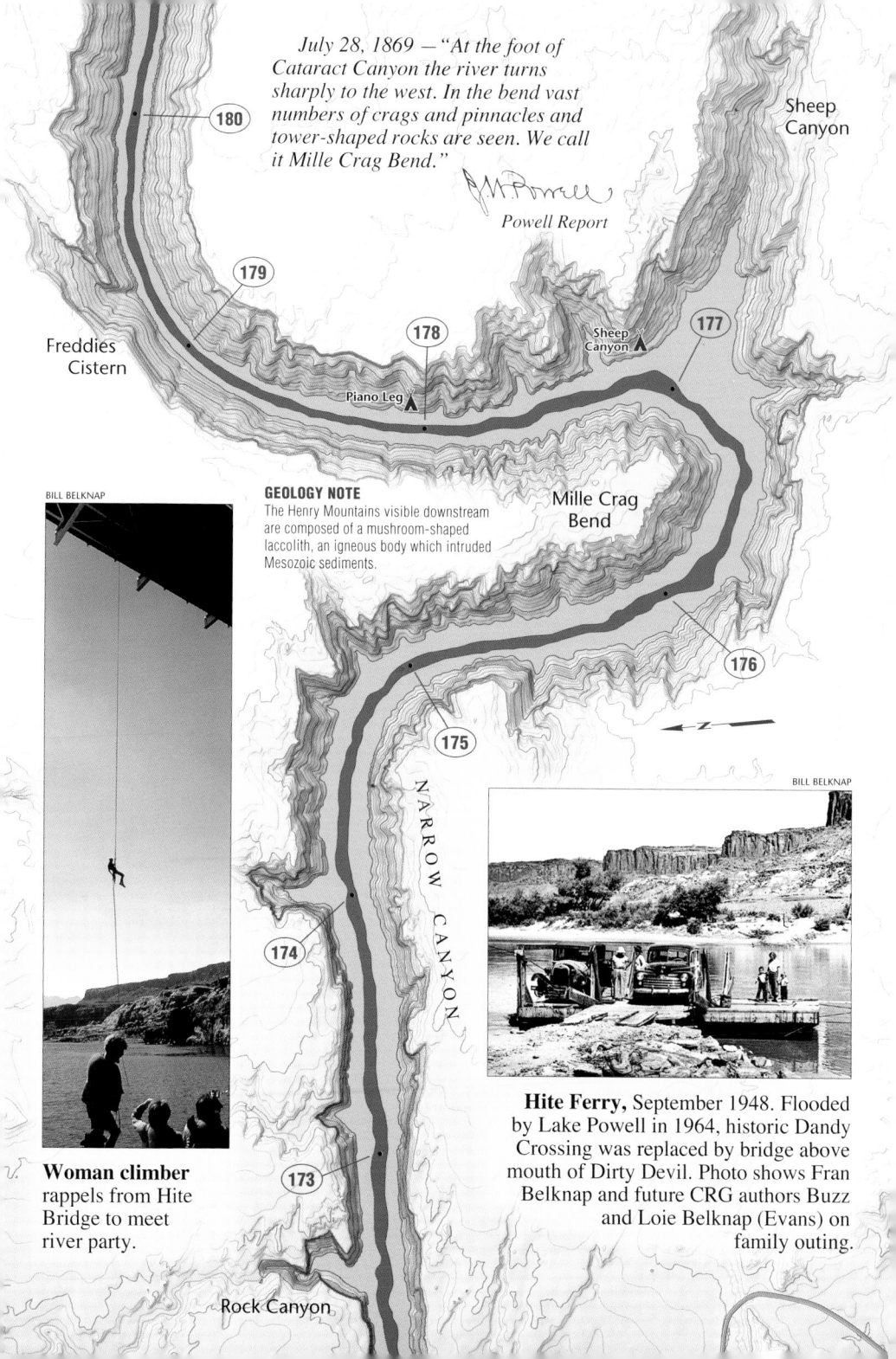

Hite Ferry, September 1948. Flooded by Lake Powell in 1964, historic Dandy Crossing was replaced by bridge above mouth of Dirty Devil. Photo shows Fran Belknap and future CRG authors Buzz and Loie Belknap (Evans) on family outing.

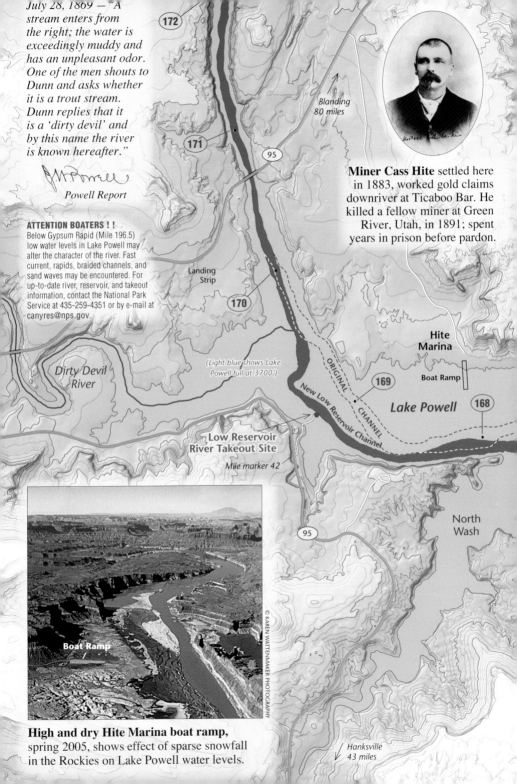

July 28, 1869 — "A stream enters from the right; the water is exceedingly muddy and has an unpleasant odor. One of the men shouts to Dunn and asks whether it is a trout stream. Dunn replies that it is a 'dirty devil' and by this name the river is known hereafter."

J. W. Powell

Powell Report

ATTENTION BOATERS ! !
Below Gypsum Rapid (Mile 196.5) low water levels in Lake Powell may alter the character of the river. Fast current, rapids, braided channels, and sand waves may be encountered. For up-to-date river, reservoir, and takeout information, contact the National Park Service at 435-259-4351 or by e-mail at canyres@nps.gov.

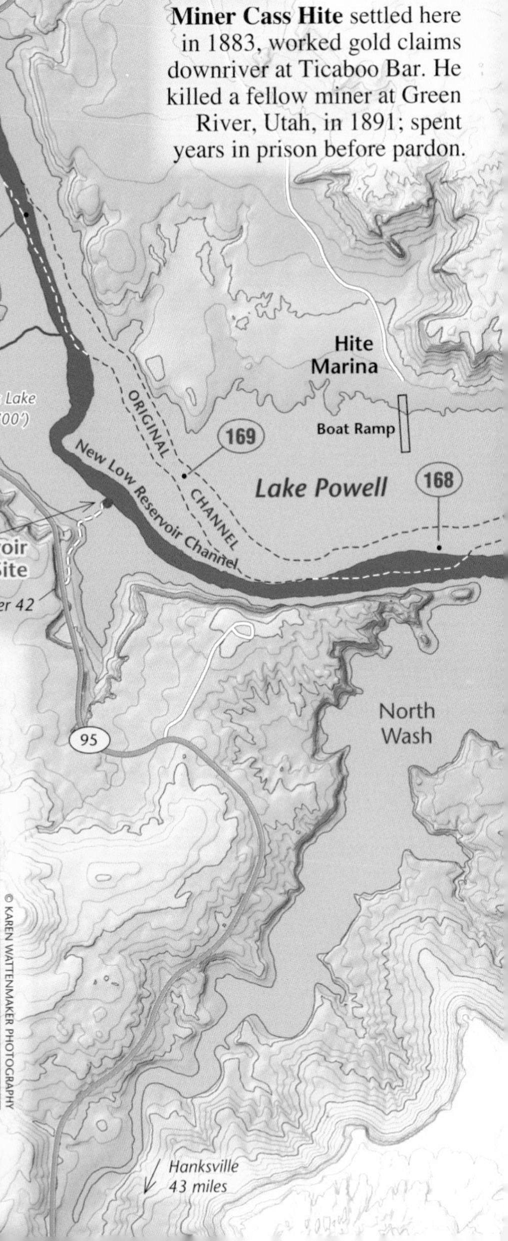

Miner Cass Hite settled here in 1883, worked gold claims downriver at Ticaboo Bar. He killed a fellow miner at Green River, Utah, in 1891; spent years in prison before pardon.

© KAREN WATTENMAKER PHOTOGRAPHY

High and dry Hite Marina boat ramp, spring 2005, shows effect of sparse snowfall in the Rockies on Lake Powell water levels.

"But miracle or error the dam is there, and we can only learn its lesson—and enjoy Lake Powell."

Bill Belknap

BILL BELKNAP

"To an astronaut, the nine-trillion-gallon reservoir of Lake Powell rising behind Glen Canyon Dam would resemble a gigantic bolt of forked lightning spread across the Arizona-Utah desert," wrote Walter Edwards in *National Geographic*. "To some people, it represents irrigation, flood control, electric power, recreating, and beauty—a man-made miracle. To others it demonstrates the ways in which the splendor of nature, revealed through eons of geologic change, can be drowned by the works of man in an instant of cosmic time—a tragic error."

But miracle or error the dam is there, and we can only learn its lessons—and enjoy Lake Powell.

When you first glance at it on a map you tend to think that with a fast boat and a half a day you could see most of Lake Powell. But a close check reveals it's over 180-miles long, with dozens of canyons and countless coves, bays, inlets—and a shoreline of more than 1800 miles. And "seeing" Lake Powell becomes an exploration project that could fill vacations for years to come. Finding your way among Lake Powell's maze of similar canyons can be a real challenge, especially your first time out. But following the main channel is fairly simple: the National Park Service has installed a series of numbered buoys which show the approximate distance in miles uplake from Glen Canyon Dam.

At its maximum elevation the lake drowns all of the rapids in the last 35 miles of Cataract Canyon—heartbreaking to river runners but a real plus if you're a power boater bent on exploring side canyons. In at least two of these—Dark Canyon and Clearwater—spring-fed streams run year round, cascading over ledges and forming

House Boating is a popular activity on Lake Powell. Thousands each year enjoy the lake from their rented "home."

ARAMARK/Lake Powell Resorts & Marinas

irresistible swimming holes.

Slickrock camping is a surprising Lake Powell feature. While you're free to camp almost anywhere around its smoothly eroded shoreline, finding a patch of level ground can be a problem. But nestled among the expanses of bare sandstone are comfortably shaped campsites—often protected from the wind—where you can anchor a boat and lay out bedrolls.

Thousands of photos are taken each year of Lake Powell's kaleidoscopic reflections. Where else in the world do you find apparently endless red sandstone cliffs, striped with browns and blacks and buffs, symmetrically mirrored in dark blue water?

While Lake Powell's rising waters covered many prehistoric Indian ruins, more were carefully excavated and recorded before being flooded. But the lake also brought easy access to a number of formerly hard-to-get-at archaeological sites such as 700-year-old Defiance House in Forgotten Canyon.

Glen Canyon National Recreation Area

For helpful information about boating, fishing, sailing, camping, hiking, and Rainbow Bridge National Monument, contact 928-608-6404 or www.nps.gov/glca.

The town of Page was literally built from scratch on a desert mesa in the mid-1950s to provide homes and some semblance of community life for the construction workers of Glen Canyon Dam. It lived to become the shopping and service center to Lake Powell and Glen Canyon National Recreation Area.

The Bureau of Reclamation operates Glen Canyon Dam and its powerplant. The National Park Service manages the Carl Hayden Visitor Center and administers Glen Canyon National Recreation Area and Lake Powell.

Visitor information contact (928) 608-6404 or www.nps.gov/glca.

BILL BELKNAP

BILL BELKNAP

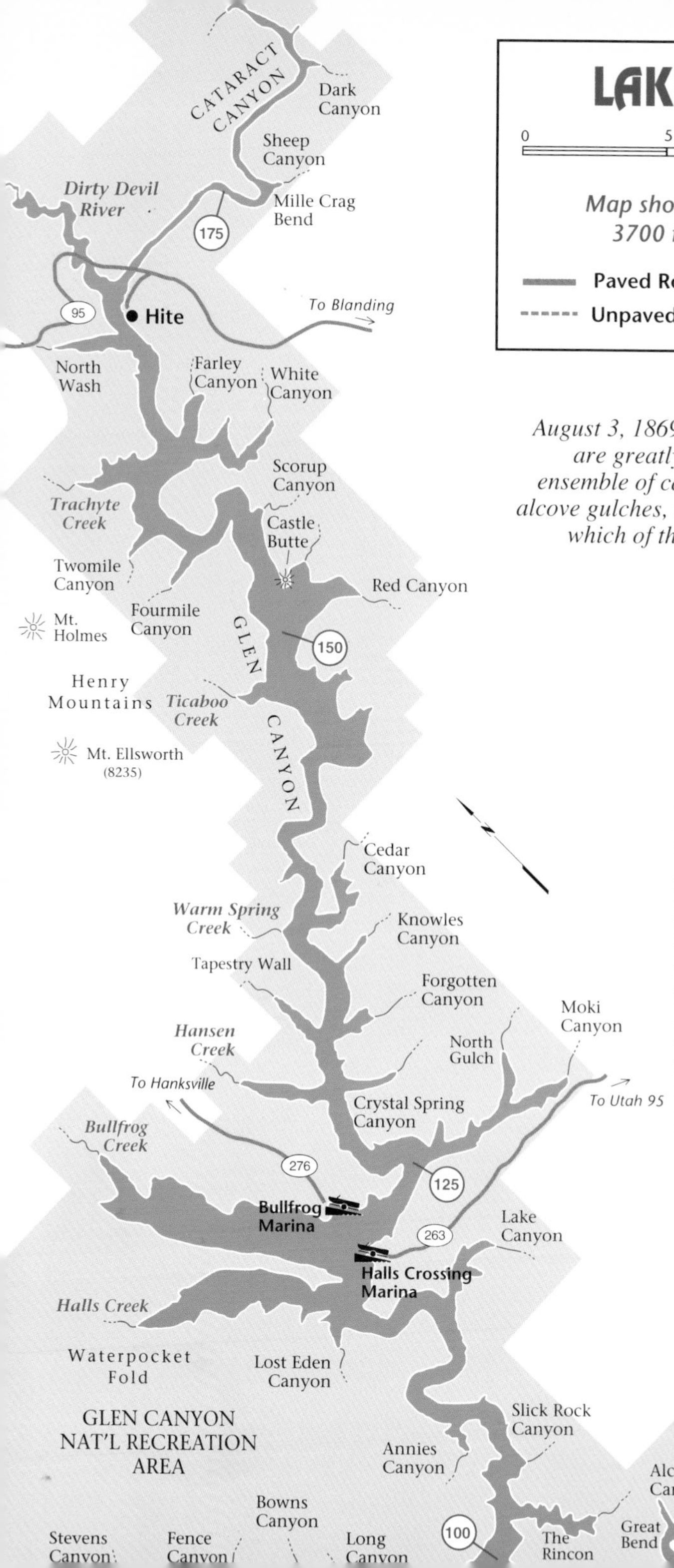

August 3, 1869 – "The features of this canyon are greatly diversified. We have a curious ensemble of carved walls, royal arches, glens, alcove gulches, mounds, and monuments. From which of these shall we select a name? We decide to call it Glen Canyon."

J.W. Powell

Powell Report

BILL BELKNAP

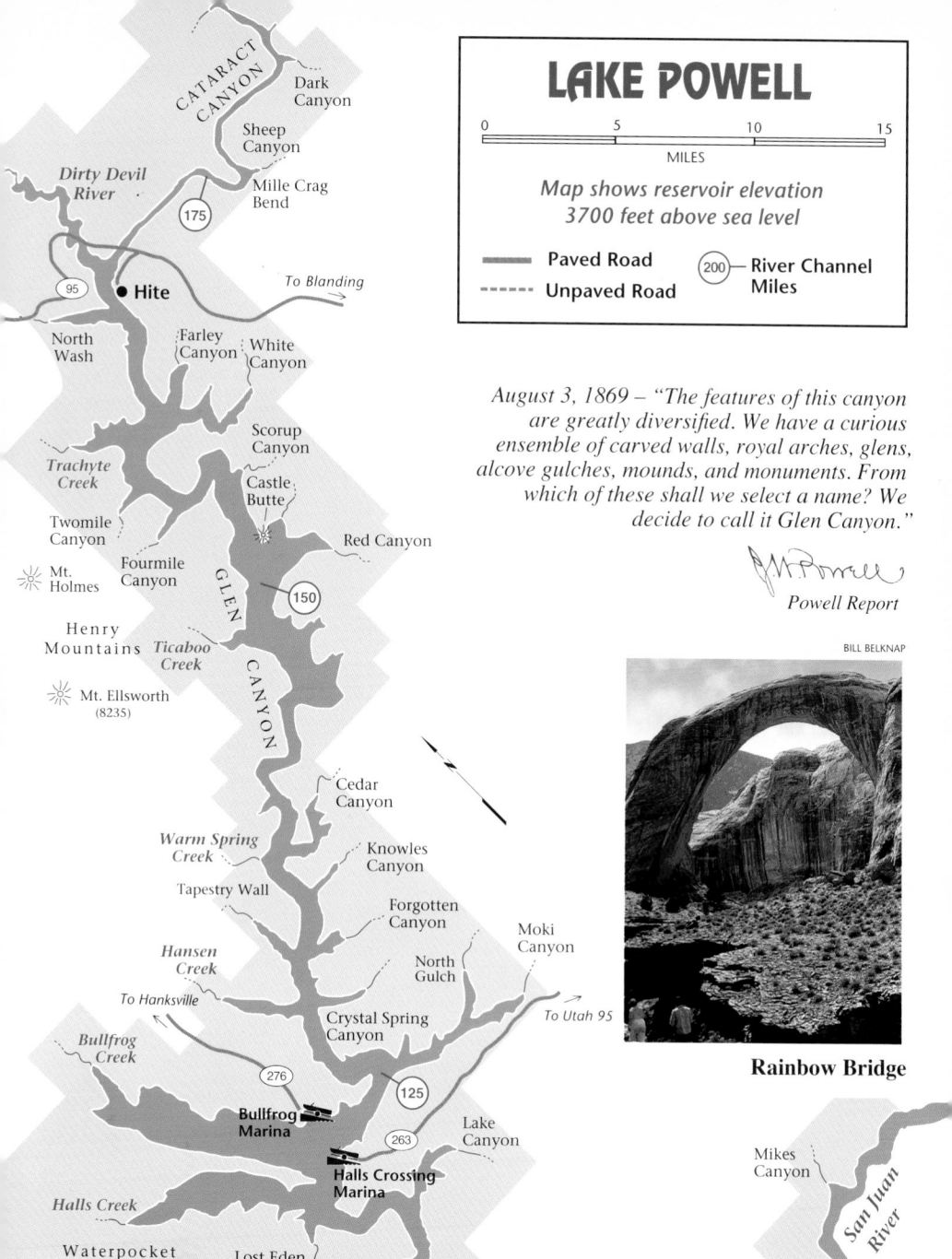

Rainbow Bridge

Escalante River
Deep Canyon
Wilson Creek
Desha Canyon
Willow Creek
Davis Gulch
Clear Creek
Hole-in-the-Rock
Cottonwood Canyon
Cha Canyon
To Escalante
Reflection Canyon
75
Hidden Passage
Nasja Creek
Anasazi Canyon
Twilight Canyon
Kaiparowits Plateau
Oak Canyon
Navajo Mountain
(10,388)
Cascade Canyon
RAINBOW BRIDGE NAT'L MON.
Dangling Rope Canyon
Forbidding Canyon
Dangling Rope Marina
Middle Rock Creek
Dry Rock Creek
Aztec Creek
Rock Creek
Cathedral Canyon
Wetherill Canyon
GLEN CANYON NAT'L RECREATION AREA
Dungeon Canyon
UTAH
ARIZONA
Last Chance Creek
50
West Canyon
Gregory Butte
Padre Canyon
Gunsight Butte
Padre Point
Gunsight Canyon
NAVAJO INDIAN RESERVATION
GLEN CANYON
Labyrinth Canyon
Warm Creek
Tower Butte
Navajo Creek
25
Wahweap Marina
Antelope Point Marina
Antelope Creek
22
To Kaibito
To Kanab
Glen Canyon Dam
PAGE
Colorado River
89
Lees Ferry
Paria River
0

BILL BELKNAP

Buck Whitehat,
Navajo Indian

BILL BELKNAP

Navajo Mountain in background

GLEN CANYON

Good fishing, clear cold water, and multicolored canyon walls reward visitors along this 15-mile stretch between Glen Canyon Dam and Lees Ferry. There's access from either end; you can go upriver from Lees Ferry or downriver from the dam on a half-day guided float trip aboard a large pontoon raft.

Historic Lees Ferry lies between Glen and Marble canyons, and from the early 1870s until 1929 was the only vehicle crossing in some 500 miles. Today thousands of people throughout the world remember Lees Ferry as the starting point of a highlight in their lives—a Grand Canyon river trip.

Write National Park Service, Glen Canyon National Recreation Area, P.O. Box 1507, Page AZ 86040 (928) 608-6200 for information on this section or visit website at www.nps.gov/glca. For a list of outfitters offering Grand Canyon river trips, write River Permits Office, Grand Canyon National Park, P.O. Box 129, Grand Canyon, AZ 86023 (928) 638-7843 or call toll free: (800) 959-9164. Visit website at www.nps.gov/grca/river/index.htm.

Above photo: Looking downstream from Glen Canyon Dam into Glen Canyon's steep red walls. BUREAU OF RECLAMATION

RIVER FLOW INFORMATION
CALL: 801-539-1311 or go to www.cbrfc.noaa.gov/

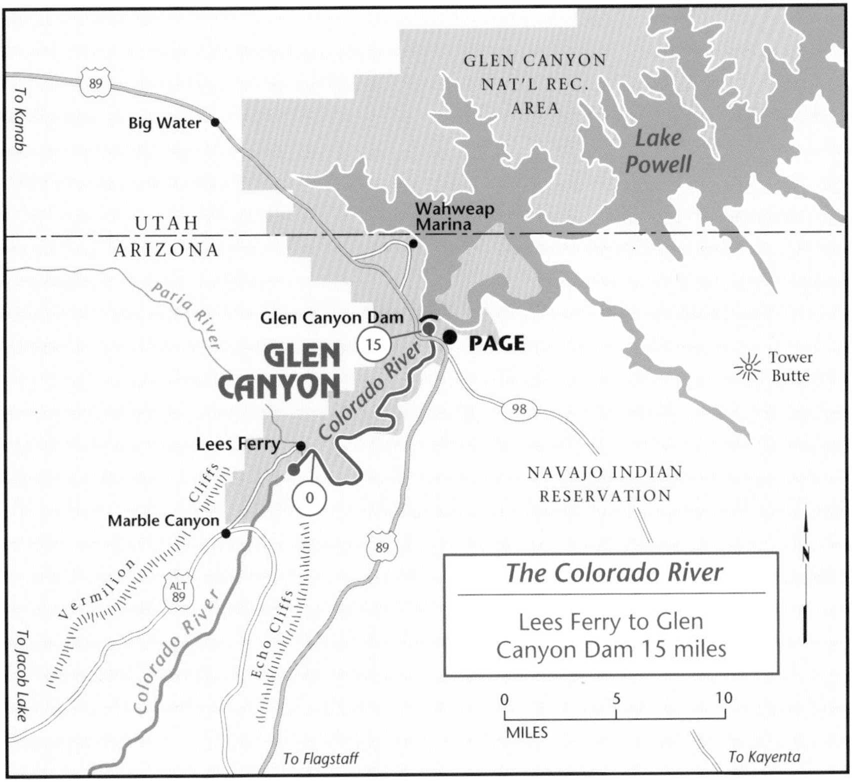

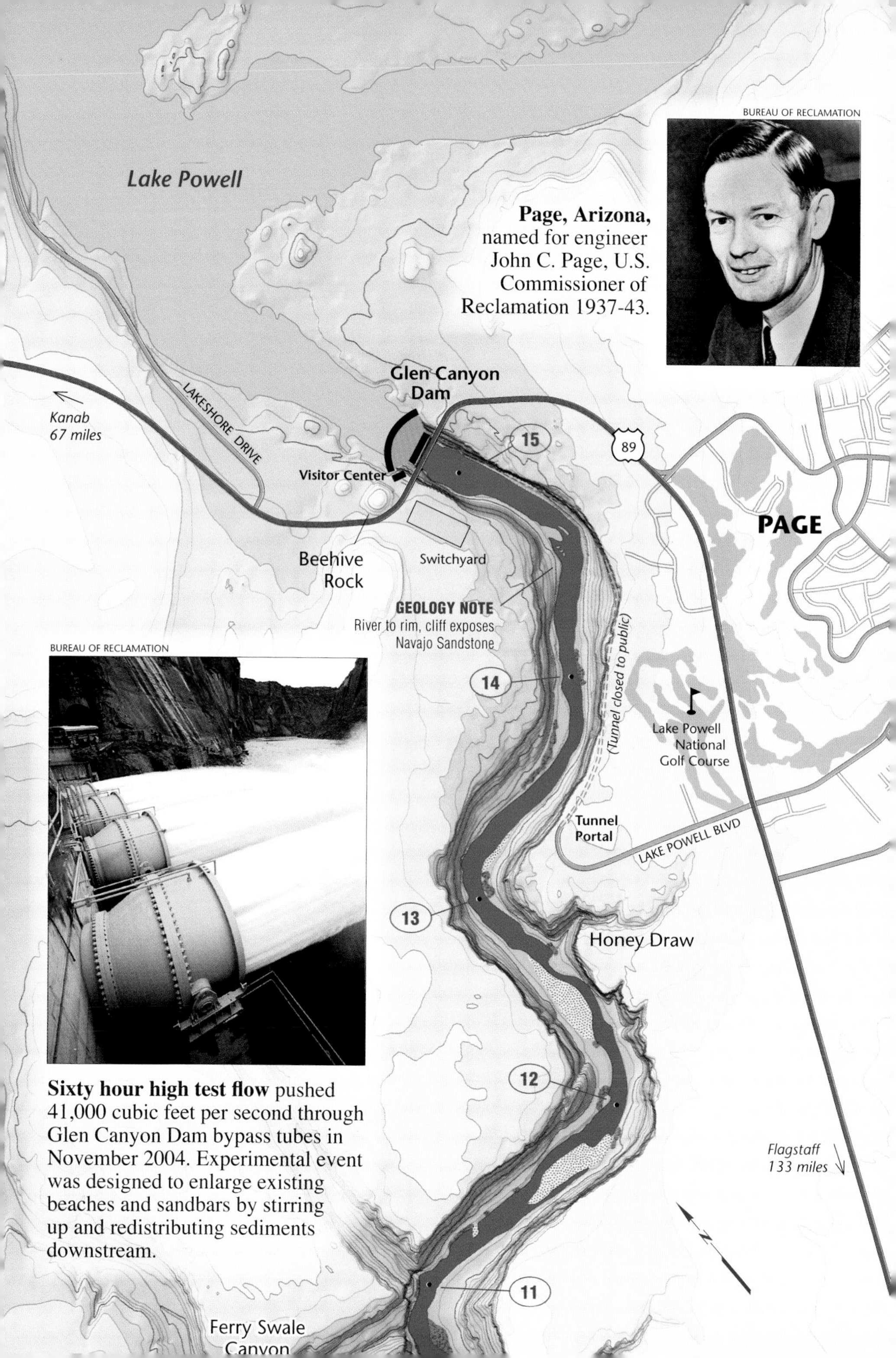

BUREAU OF RECLAMATION

Page, Arizona, named for engineer John C. Page, U.S. Commissioner of Reclamation 1937-43.

BUREAU OF RECLAMATION

Sixty hour high test flow pushed 41,000 cubic feet per second through Glen Canyon Dam bypass tubes in November 2004. Experimental event was designed to enlarge existing beaches and sandbars by stirring up and redistributing sediments downstream.

RSTON COLLECTION

computer colorized image

Ringing for the ferryman, Lees Ferry 1923.

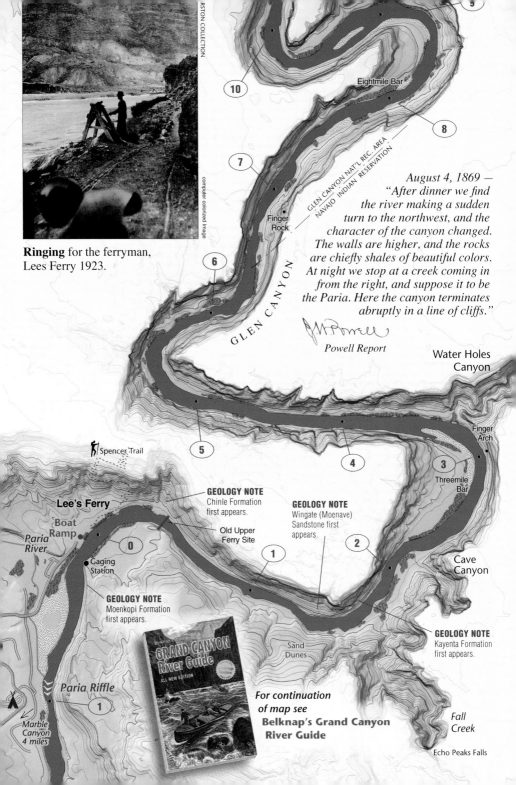

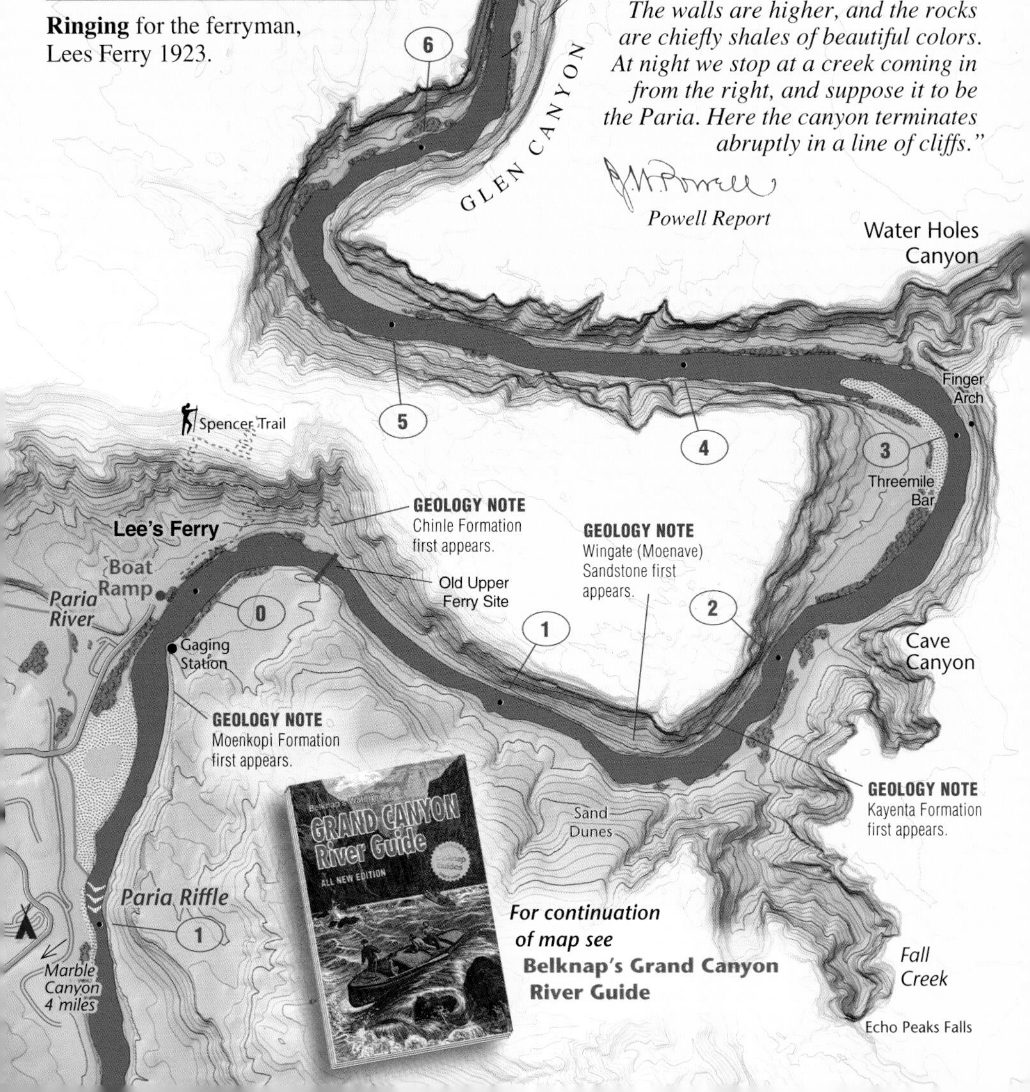

August 4, 1869 –
"After dinner we find the river making a sudden turn to the northwest, and the character of the canyon changed. The walls are higher, and the rocks are chiefly shales of beautiful colors. At night we stop at a creek coming in from the right, and suppose it to be the Paria. Here the canyon terminates abruptly in a line of cliffs."

J.W. Powell

Powell Report

For continuation of map see Belknap's Grand Canyon River Guide

RIVER LOG

BILL BELKNAP